I want to dedicate this book to three of the most important people in my life; Iain, my husband and my rock, who has been forever there as a support through thick and thin, and Laura, my daughter, wonderful mother and daughter and talented photographer (www.lovelaughbelieve.com). And finally, this is a book that has been about some of the trials, but also the joys of motherhood, so I also dedicate this book to my mum, who I just love for being my mum.

Journey To Chocolate
is written and published by Ann Girling
copyright ©2011 Ann Girling

Copyright

Contents

Acknowledgements

Firstly I want to thank you, the reader, for reading this book and taking the time out for the *Moments to Ponder*. I really hope that it will set you off on your journey to wherever you want to be.

There are so many people I want to thank, because without them, this story and this book would never have become a reality. So let me start with my therapist, Angela Duplessis (Cameron), who set me off on my journey with her wonderful and loving care over a period of two long and painful years. Then there's my coach, Tony Barton (www.redkitecoaching.com) who helped me believe in myself and has challenged me and still does challenge me to step right out of my comfort zone. Through him I have learnt so much about coaching too, including the fun side! Also, I want to thank all the wonderful people I met through my coach training with the Coaches Training Institute (www.thecoaches.com).

Then there are the people who helped make this book happen: Lizzie Gates (www.lonelyfurrowcompany.com) with her great writing courses and coaching, through whom I learnt the joy of writing; Jeremy Bassett (www.corveconsultancy.com) my harshest critic but whose feedback on my blogs made me really believe that I could write; Shelli Walsh (www.shellshockdesign.co.uk) who took on the task of designing the book and getting it printed at the last minute and did it; Julie Morrisroe (www.cosmicworkshop.co.uk) who designed my beautiful brand and has produced the illustrations for the book; and finally there is Mary Newsome, who had the difficult task of proof-reading and giving me the final feedback which has helped me make this book the best it can be.

Last but not least I have to thank the inspirational Elaine Hanzak-Gott (www.hanzak.com), who through her book *Eyes without Sparkle*, made me realise that we all have stories that are worthy of telling. And I thank her so much for writing the foreword to this book.

x

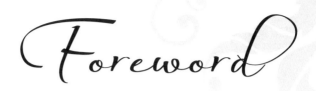
Foreword

A journey is defined in the Oxford English Dictionary as:

'the act of going from one place to another; distance travelled'.

I am honoured, delighted and grateful that Ann Girling's journey and mine have connected, initially with a first conversation by telephone whilst I was at King's Cross station, having been interviewed by Ruby Wax for the BBC.

Through our various networking events in the north-west of England, several people had suggested that Ann and I connected as we both shared a passion for postnatal illness and for helping others affected by it. That first phone call in 2008 led to us meeting for a coffee at my home, which was only a few miles away from hers. Since that time we have continued on our individual journeys but increasingly we are travelling together in a joint purpose and deepening friendship.

I have never been invited to write a foreword for a book before, so I was humbled and proud to be asked by Ann. Over the last few years Ann has often commented *It will be in my book* – whether it be a thought, word or deed! So often she has said she was *working on her book* and now it is finally here! She invites us to share her journey (so far) and in doing so it helps us to shape our own with greater empowerment, freedom, choice and ultimately pleasure.

Ann always believed that in our joint workshops which we deliver around postnatal illness, that I was the most important one! In her mind I was the one with the published book *Eyes without Sparkle – a journey through postnatal illness* (Radcliffe, 2005); the more dramatic story and the title of international speaker. Yet I believed that she was the most important one because not only did she have her experiences to offer but also official qualifications to her name!

In essence we are a team – we complement one another. We

support each other. We praise one another. We kick each other up the backside when needed. We have a healthy element of competition. For example, as experts registered with www.greatvine.com we tease who receives a message first! I was impressed by how well read Ann is, something I feel I am not! Another reason we are a good team.

Often personal development books are written *at* us – we are supposed to think that these perceived 'greater beings' have all the right answers and we are failing and useless in some way. The authors and speakers appear 'to have it all'. Ann writes about herself, but with us and for us, in a way that as a woman makes you think *me too*. She inspires by sharing aspects of her journey which have been painful and that inspires us to take action from where we are in life right now, to where we would like to be.

As women, our whole lives consist of change from puberty: periods, possibly marriage, babies, menopause, career et cetera. Part of change means loss of expectation, opportunities, physical aspects and more. Ann takes us through several changes she has faced and how she dealt with them either successfully or otherwise.

Both Ann and I are self-employed after careers in the public sector, myself as a special needs teacher and Ann in nursing roles. Both of us felt our creativity and passion was crushed in those professions in the latter years. We can now embrace our individuality and both have colour and sparkle in our lives – we both laughed that we have the identical Filofax, me in red, she in pink. We share a delight in fun, bright *Radley* handbags and colourful clothes when we work, against a sea of black and grey! We both love to wander in wide, open spaces. Most importantly, we celebrate and value who we are and what our experiences can do to help others.

You will read about our workshops towards the end of the book, but I feel I wish to expand on the *peak moment* we experienced in a recent one. Ann and I have integrity in what we do and for the first and only time, I had to admit that holding a workshop four days after my partner and soul mate died, was too much and it was postponed.

Many times we had discussed that the symptoms and aids to recovery from depression and bereavement were the same. Loss is at the heart of many aspects of human challenge. I never appreciated this until Clive died six months ago. I shared my experiences of puerperal psychosis, a severe form of postnatal illness, because I wanted to give others hope. I wanted to show how a woman who appeared to 'have it all' – a wanted, healthy baby; supportive husband and family; comfortable home; good career – could lose it and become a mental wreck needing psychiatric care in hospital, but then make a full recovery. As a result of my book my journey changed; it heralded a new career, the breakdown of my marriage and then onto a new, incredibly romantic and powerful new relationship. Being the best Mum I can be, to my son now 15, remains paramount to me.

Ann travelled with me these last couple of years and we both learnt from Clive, who was also a speaker, author and personal development specialist. Two weeks before he died, he saw Ann and I present together when he was Master of Ceremonies at the launch of The Joanne (Joe) Bingley Memorial Foundation, of which we are both trustees. We were delighted that he approved of what he saw and recognised that we actually both have bright lights to shine but together they are even brighter.

Ann writes about changes and loss. At 47 I did not expect to experience either this year, but then I had to when Clive unexpectedly died. The workshop was rearranged and we had around 30 delegates attached to Children's Centres in Doncaster. We also had Chris Bingley, the founder of the Joanne (Joe) Bingley Memorial Foundation and Joe's widower and Dinah, another trustee with us. Joe had taken her own life, 10 weeks after giving birth to their daughter Emily. Part of the aims of the Foundation are to raise awareness and educate around postnatal illness so tragedies like Joe's are avoided in future.

Paradoxically, Ann had experienced a massive change in her life with the arrival of her first grandson, the gorgeous Jacob. I do not think Ann expected the massive wave of love and emotion that followed. She had spent some time with the new family in Germany and was feeling the mixture of emotions of incredible bonding with Jacob, pride in her daughter and also the pain in not seeing them! She was aching to cuddle her grandson, I was aching for Clive's arms around me! And we had Chris aching for Joe!

By the end of the day we all felt that we had delivered our most amazing workshop to date. Yes we raised awareness of the signs, symptoms, causes of postnatal depression and offered some ways to help those affected – and not just the mothers. We had tears and also laughter. Yet the overwhelming benefit at the end of the day was the feedback (or should it be feed forward?) when we invited delegates to share their key learning. We were blown away by the comments.

Many had truly absorbed our message, that in order to be effective in helping others you *have* to look after yourself more. For example, one lady said she would be arranging a treat for a friend whose mother has a terminal illness. Random acts of kindness would be forthcoming in many directions as a result of that workshop!

Like Ann, that day for me was incredible on many levels, not least that through our ability and willingness to share our experiences we can give others the permission and tools to make their lives happier and more fulfilled in their wide ranging roles in life. I have also observed a difference in Ann since she became a grandmother – her emotions are much nearer the surface. I rarely saw tears in her eyes before Jacob, now I do, but they are balanced with a brightness and sparkle too. He has her eyes too! It is beautiful to see and I am thrilled to have been part of that journey.

At the same time my eyes are often filled with tears, but I am on my next journey to get my sparkle back.

One quote that Ann cites is from Kalil Galbrain who says "*Your work is your love made visible*". Ann's writing shows us she has an abundance of both to give and deserves to receive.

Ann's book and her journey have reminded me that it's not just me who has a loss and that it is okay to grieve and express my feelings. Also, that although life is a rollercoaster, with support around you and the realisation that you have a personal responsibility to be in the driving seat, there can be plenty of chocolate along the way. I look forward to sharing many boxes with her!

We are all going from one place to another and the journey is easier if you choose the right people to travel with.

Who are you taking with you?

Elaine Hanzak-Gott
www.hanzak.com
August 2011

Introduction

It was 11 years ago in the year 2000, that I reached my 50th birthday. I was quite happy to do that, it didn't faze me in any way and I felt I had everything I wanted in my life: a lovely home, a wonderful and supportive husband and a daughter about to go out and make her mark in the world. I also had a challenging and rewarding career as professional lead for health visiting in the NHS; I felt it was a job for life and would serve me well for the next 10 years when I would receive my pension – a just reward for all those years working in the NHS.

What I didn't realise was that a number of life events, ranging from the impact of going to boarding school, through mild postnatal depression, through secondary infertility, through a miscarriage had left me with the need to grieve for the various things I had lost; my happy childhood, the joy of being a mother, the completion of my family and the baby I longed for. However, I had never allowed myself to do so. My way of coping was to keep busy, that way I never had to feel those intensely painful feelings which were stuffed down in the bin of my mind. But inevitably the time came when the emotional bin was full and the lid burst open, and I had to face those feelings. I had to confront the guilt, the lost confidence and low self-esteem and most of all the pain of those losses.

But it has all been worth it. The years since have been amazing as I have rebuilt my life both personally and professionally and found my real purpose for being in the world. I know that my story is no different from many other women's and I wanted to share it to inspire others to follow a similar journey. Underpinning all of this is my philosophy that if we, as women, could step more happily and more confidently into our female energy, bringing our values of caring and nurturing to the world, a more harmonious balance would be created. The world would then become a safer and more vibrant place for ourselves, for our children and for our grandchildren.

I have written about the *emotional rollercoaster of motherhood* and I question society's pressure on women. You will feel the pain of my loss after miscarriage and the experience of suffering from stress-related depression, some would call it near burnout. You will also see how I challenge the way western medicine views postnatal depression and mental health as a whole. I also want you to share the joy I experienced seeing my daughter married and, in particular, the birth of my grandson. I have included her story as a postscript to my own.

My intention in writing this book is that it doesn't fit into the typical 'self-help' category. I am disturbed by the numbers of books that suggest that by reading them you can change your life in a week. I don't believe that. Deep and lasting change takes much longer and I doubt whether we can ever say that that work is done. I was reminded of this only recently by a friend who told me about a book called *Zero Limits* by Joe Vitale in which he uses an image of a room to illustrate his point. He describes how, by learning more about ourselves, and through the way we treat ourselves, we clean out that room from top to bottom. But if, after having done that, we leave it and ignore it, it becomes dusty and neglected again. The strong message is we need to be constantly in the business of self-care.

How to use this book

I notice that many books like this have a *how to use this book* section. As far as I'm concerned, this book is a story and stories need to be read from the beginning to the end. However, you will find at the end of each chapter a *Moments to Ponder* section where there are some reflective questions or some actions to take which I have used for myself and also for my clients and have found to be effective. They will help with providing you with more insight, greater confidence, direction and focus, and also self-care.

What I have also done is research various aspects of my story. If you like, use myself as a case study and the reason for doing that is that, even if you don't share my experiences, your responses to events in your life will be very similar to my own. I want you to have those *Me too* moments when you will realise that you are not alone. You will find all my sources referenced, the bracketed numbers referring to a list at the end of the book.

What you may find you want to do, so that you don't lose the thread of the story, is to keep reading the book to the end and then come back to those *Moments to Ponder*. By doing that it may be that you feel more inspired to do the work, but I leave it up to you. As in so many things in life there is no right or wrong way. I just want you to use this book in the way that works best for you. As I have already said, I have not used the phrase 'self-help' because I strongly feel that to make real changes in our lives, we need the help of another who will be with us wherever we are at, hear what we are saying and what we are feeling, and see who we truly are. That is the joy of working with a fully qualified and accredited coach. However, these reflective interludes will help you start on your journey.

Most of all, it is my hope that you will enjoy my journey and then set out on your own.

Ann Girling
August 2011

Chapter 1

Growing up

Do you often wonder what makes you tick and why? Why some things really annoy you or why you get really passionate about something else, and at other times you feel absolutely on top of the world? At other times your world just doesn't feel right, something's grating, you might even feel stressed or burnt out. You lack meaning and purpose in your life. At the heart of these events are your values, sometimes they're being honoured, at other times they most definitely are not.

This chapter is about values:

- What they are
- How they show up
- I'm even going to theorise about what they are and where they come from; are we born with them?
- How to clarify what some of your values are
- How we make up stories about ourselves

This chapter also acts as an introduction to me and my story. It wasn't initially my intention to write about my childhood, as I didn't see its relevance in the message I wanted to get over. There was nothing special about it. But maybe that's the whole point as we often read stories about people whose childhoods have been blighted by some kind of drama, abuse, illness and the like. My story is one of a happy childhood but that doesn't mean in any way it somehow has less meaning. My experience is shared by many and you may also recognise, as I now do, the time when childhood ends and you are faced with the realities of life, as I did when I was just 13.

Stories

It was when I read the opening words from Lynn Serafinn's book *The Garden of the Soul* [1] that I realised how much there is to learn from those early years that will help us learn for the future:

> "*You are already the hero of your own life. You did not earn this title. You did not have to. You were born the hero. It is your birthright. If you do not take up your birthright, no one else will do it for you. If you leave it unclaimed, the universe will remain bereft of something it passionately desires. The world will continue to long for that which only you can fulfil. It will dream of you again and again. It will call you repeatedly. It will cry for you.*
>
> *Then, one day, in this lifetime or the next, or the next after that, you will finally take up the path of least resistance to the self, and simply become the person you were always meant to be. And on that day, ever so easily, you will see that you were always the hero of this story – your story – and that all you ever needed in order to be the hero, was to look within the simple stories of your own life.*" [1, p3]

Do you feel that you are the *hero of your own life*? If you are who would you be? Where would you look for the answers? This is part of the discovery I hope you will make through working with the exercises in this book.

First we will start with my 'simple stories' which I will relate here, the simple stories that help me understand what I'm about. The place I started to look was in my childhood and I discovered so many clues there as to what was important to me: my values. This is where I want you to start your journey by looking for your values and the exercise at the end of the chapter will help you do that. You cannot start to think about where you want to go in your life if you don't know where you are starting from and this chapter is about learning about you and what matters to you.

Also note that I use the word *stories* and it is often in our childhood we start to develop other stories that we carry with us into our adult lives, stories that we believe to be the truth about ourselves. What I want you to know is that stories are not fact but fiction and can be rewritten, just as I am redrafting this book. It's at that point that I will introduce the term 'saboteur'. I want you to start recognising the voice of your saboteur so that you can disarm him/her/them.

My Childhood

I am the eldest of three children, born into post war austerity with rationing still in force. We didn't have a lot of spare money but that really didn't seem to matter to me at least. My father was still undergoing his training to become a chartered accountant. I am astonished that now more than 60 years after they married, my parents still have the dining room table they bought, one of their biggest buys – obviously built to last! Their first toaster only *died* a few years ago! In this day of materialism it is amazing how they did without something until they could afford it. We had no television until I was about 8 but we would go round to our neighbour's to watch our favourite programmes! It was about the same time that we had our first car. My mother appeared to us as a full-time mum. However, she is likely to become quite indignant if I was to suggest this, as I believe she did some secretarial work for a publishing company. The fact that I was unaware can only be a compliment to her ability to mix work and parenting. My brother arrived two years after me and we were playmates for each other, but as with all siblings not always in harmony.

I only remember the first 12 years of my life as being happy, fun and free and, as I've already said, events after that really rocked my lovely secure world. My father's strong value of education meant that we were all educated throughout our school careers in the private sector and that can't have been without a degree of financial hardship to my parents. This contrasted strongly (as I have only recently discovered) with my mother's strongly socialist principles. She would rather we had spent our secondary school years at the local grammar school. I often wonder what my outcome would have been had that happened; it feels like a *Sliding Doors* moment. I was sent off to boarding school with my full agreement. I was an avid reader and had read all Enid Blyton's books about the *Twins at Saint Clares*. I was incredibly unhappy, I missed home terribly and after one term begged to be taken away. My parents made the decision that in the interests of my education I should remain there until I had completed my O levels. The outcome was that I underachieved and, as a consequence, one of the stories I made up was that I didn't have the ability to achieve academically as compared to my siblings.

If I add to this the fact that we relocated 200 miles away from my home during that time and my baby sister was born, here were two major life events, the impact of which I only see as I look back over the years. I now see that these events affected my educational attainment and my emotional development. At a time when most adolescents are spending time with their peer group, I was in an all girls boarding school. Boys were a complete 'no, no'! In fact, girls who were caught talking to members of the opposite sex were known to be expelled. Crushes on older girls were common; it was all part of the school culture. I have no idea if any of those crushes became sexual or were just a normal part of growing up. I was far too naïve! When I was at home I didn't have a peer group. I didn't know anyone apart from the 'boy next door' and of course I had a crush on him but it never went further than that! However, my sixth form years were spent at a girls' day school and I began to develop a peer group, although again that was hard as most peer groups were already formed. I did, however, befriend another girl who was also new in the sixth-form. We have stayed in contact ever since through our nursing careers and then through me becoming godmother to her first child

I also want to say that, in terms of my schooling, I know that my parents felt they were doing the best for me, which is all any of us can ask of our parents. As for the move, my father obtained a fantastic job promotion which must have given them much more financial freedom and they had their third child which they had longed for, for many years. It took us to Cheshire which has been home to my parents ever since and is now my home again; a place where I feel more at home than I have done for years. And for that I am grateful.

How my values were showing up

Here are a few simple stories of my life which I believe illustrate how my values were showing up. Maybe you will start to recall similar moments in your childhood too but this comes with a health warning, because for some of us, looking back to our childhood can bring up painful memories. If this does happen to you please ask for help from your GP or you may need to find a counsellor or to contact the Samaritans.

In those years leading up to boarding school I had such fun. My main memory is one of the amazing freedom we had. My best friend, Hazel, who I've recently rediscovered on Facebook, and I spent hours together. We would roam the woods collecting specimens for our nature collection we kept in the loft above my parents' garage.

I remember one day in particular where we discovered a tyre by a stagnant pond with a small island in the middle. We used that tyre as our boat and got over to the island. I think we fell in on the way back and were not well received by our mothers. Sadly, children are no longer able to have this freedom, although I am sure the dangers were no less to us then than they are now. We have just become so much more aware of them. It wasn't until the 1980's, when the Cleveland abuse scandal broke, that sexual abuse was talked about and it became every parents' fear. Sexual abuse has always happened and it is usually a person close to the family who is the abuser. The myth that strangers are potential predators gets in the way of children experiencing this same kind of freedom. I say this because if Hazel and I decided to take the wood route home from school, we had to run past a caravan in which we had made up that a witch lived. I have no idea who lived in that caravan; I'm not sure anyone did but we were never in anyway threatened by anyone.

Compare that with these words when my sense of freedom was compromised by the restrictions and rules of a girls' boarding school in the 1960's.

"I feel so alone, I feel trapped. I hate this place. Look at the walls around me that keep me in. The rules, the rules. Don't talk, don't run. Chapel twice a day. I still see the old chaplain saying the rituals of the communion now and I hear his voice when I go to a communion service. Prep. Games, oh how I hate games. Lacrosse: it's such a nasty game. I don't really have any friends here, I don't belong. The constant fear that if I don't do well I'll have to stay down and repeat a year and then there's 'the list'. If you're good enough you get to be on the list and then you get to be allowed out into the town. But break any rules and you're delisted and if you get caught talking to a boy, well that's the worst thing. I long for Ascension Day, we have an extra day out and I remember going to Virginia Water and the colours, there must have been rhododendrons and azaleas in bloom. After our Confirmation Service we have an extra day out with our parents. Outside there's a feeling of light, inside it's bleak and dark, no space, the indignity of dormitories".

I recently wrote the following story illustrating our family holidays but written through the eyes of an old fisherman. I hope you don't mind me including it but I do because I feel it again illustrates my sense of freedom and nature, and maybe fun as well.

The Fisherman's Beach

An old fisherman sits alone on the beach mending his lobster pots. He looks like a fisherman should look. He has thick white hair over which he wears a navy blue cap. He keeps himself warm with a blue Guernsey sweater and the smoke from his pipe drifts across the grey skies. His peace is shattered by the arrival of a family. He doesn't mind; he loves to watch them at play as it reminds him of his lost youth and a time long gone when he too had enjoyed the freedom of childhood and the love of his parents. So he watches, and smokes his pipe, and reminisces.

He sees a little girl, aged about 6, he thinks, judging by the gap in her front teeth! She is jumping up and down in excitement. She must be cold, he feels, with just her red swimming costume on and clutching her enormous rubber ring round her waist but the cold doesn't seem to affect her. Her brother comes up behind her. he looks a bit younger and is struggling to keep up with his sister. He seems to be more sensibly dressed in blue shorts, black wellington boots and a green jumper to keep him warm and he is carrying his bucket and spade. His parents follow on behind with the usual array of towels, jumpers, buckets and spades but something he has never seen before, the father carries a garden spade! The fisherman sits up intrigued to see what is going to happen with the garden spade.

"Mummy, Mummy, please can I go into the sea, please, please, please" says the little girl excitedly. "Will you come with me, Mummy, please." The fisherman sees the long suffering mother take her trousers and jumper off and run into the sea with the little girl. "just for a short time, Ann," she says, "it's a bit cold!" As they run down to the sea together hand in hand, the sun pops through the clouds and the skies begin to clear. The fisherman can hear the screams of delight from the little girl as she jumps the waves holding on to her mother's hand.

The fisherman's eyes turn to the garden spade and he watches, intrigued, as the father begins to create one of the biggest and most intricate sand castles he has ever seen built on this beach, and he has been mending his lobster pots here for nigh on 40-50 years. The sand takes on a life of its own in the hands of this father, and the fisherman smiles to himself wondering who is getting greater entertainment out of this; the father or the son? In fact, he notices the little boy turn his back to his father's creation and just systematically filling his bucket and turning it over, making sandcastles in the more traditional way!

They are quietly and happily working, side by side, both focussed intently on their work when the mother and the little girl return and *join in the fun of creating the sand castle. The fisherman notices that the mother starts to give directions and the children run off to the rock pools and start to collect shells and stones with which they decorate the castle, which has now taken on the look of a fort with a moat all round it. They have even managed to make a bridge over the moat and there seems to be a whole system of waterways around the castle.*

He feels sure that this castle will never be completed and the edifice it has become, with its complex navigational system, oh look, the little boy is sailing his little yacht round it. Indeed he's right, as of course the sea being never still, is getting nearer to them. And now look, that amazing spade is in use again and a simple but big castle is built and on the top sits the little boy and the little girl watching as the sea swirls around them. It gets closer and closer but of course the fisherman's beach is a benign beach and the sea comes in fairly slowly. There's lots of time for this happy family to pack up all their bits and pieces and leave.

Soon after their departure, the castle and fort and all the waterworks they worked so hard to create disappear, under the rising seas. The fisherman is reminded of the fleeting nature of such things but he also takes with him the pleasure and joy that this family have given him in one afternoon, as he returns to his solitary existence.

Of course there are a myriad of other stories I could tell illustrating different values. Maybe you will start to see yours showing up in your own stories of things you loved to do as a child and when you were at your happiest.

But What are Values?

Values will be a thread going through this book as they are key to helping us take the right route on our journey, in a way acting as signposts. Values are not morals or principles, nor are they right or wrong in anyway. They are described as *"the qualities of a life fully lived from the inside out"* [2], as *"the unconscious filters used to make choices"* [3]. I see them as being as essential to our lives as our own DNA. Our values somehow define who we are. Understanding our values is essential to leading a fulfilling life.

So what shows up in the stories I have shared? Firstly, one of my top values is freedom. Freedom for me means freedom of spirit, and not being confined by walls or unnecessary rules. It does not mean freedom to do what I want, when I want, with no consideration for others. And part of that freedom is being outdoors. I am never happier than when I'm out walking or in my garden and I think that was as true for me then as it is now. I still remember the wall that surrounded my school and caused me such profound unhappiness. We had to earn the right to go outside of those walls by demonstrating impeccable behaviour and obeying somewhat arcane rules. As I have already said, you could then get on 'the list' which allowed certain privileges such as going out of that school and into the town. Any bad behaviour led to being 'delisted' and losing those privileges.

What is important to understand here is that the value word I have used, *freedom,* is only a word and it's difficult to incorporate what I mean by freedom in just the one word as I've already implied. If freedom is one of your core values then it may mean something very different. So to be clearer about it, we can use a string of words. How do I define freedom for me? I feel at my most free when I am in wide open spaces, in the fresh air, with nature and so I could define it like this: freedom/outdoors/nature/spirituality/unrestricted.

Where do our values come from?

I have become increasingly curious about values and when they start to show up. Are we born with them or are they created by the environment we grow up in? I have learnt through some of my training that certain values are associated with certain personality types. Are values and personality the same thing or are they different? As I reflected on personality, I thought about the way different babies behave. Some love to be cuddled, others love routine, there are those babies who seem very thoughtful and those who need a lot of action and entertaining. It has been argued [4] that we are indeed born with our personality traits but values are strongly influenced by the environment. This seems to evidence what I saw in different babies as a health visitor and also the fact that parents often describe their children as being as 'different as chalk and cheese' or find it unbelievable that two children could be so different and have the same parents.

There has to be a link between values and personality. The development of personality theory goes back as far as Hippocrates in 400 B.C. which for me has culminated in the work of an American, Don Lowry [5]. Within each of his colour classifications: gold, orange, blue and green, he describes the values, joys, strengths and needs of each. Values and personality are inextricably linked and are both inborn and influenced by our environment. Lowry's work is used throughout the world in large and small corporate and public sector organisations to help improve self-esteem and confidence and the way people relate to each other and to build effective teams and leaders.

There's something else I want to look at briefly. Is there something at a deeper level? are our values about our soul? If we honour our values in a more authentic way, are we feeding our soul? Let me quote from a book: *"For when the sacred, or spirituality, is experienced as lying at the heart of who you are, as coming from You it can hardly dictate or constrain who you are"*. [6, p126]. Values are who we are. I am reminded of the feeling I get when I'm out walking alone in the countryside and have that feeling of connection to nature and to something much bigger than I am. This is a topic I find endlessly fascinating and will continue to study.

Setting up our stories

Our values can be strongly influenced by those around us: our parents, school, our peer group, our career choice and our employers. In seeking for approval by those close to us, whose values may be different to our own, we may somehow judge ourselves to be wrong in some way or inferior and set the stories in motion that act as obstacles in our adult life and can significantly affect our self-esteem.

When we are young we want to be loved and accepted by those close to us. Let us use the metaphor of the world within us as being a magnificent castle [7]. It contains thousands of rooms, each room representing a different aspect of our personality. When we are children we explore each room fascinated by what we find inside. One day someone finds you in the 'lazy room' and chides you for being lazy. You want to be accepted by this person so you shut that door and never go into it again. Other doors are shut and locked in a similar way. Think of the stories that surround us as we grow up *I can't sing, I'm no good at sport, I'm not clever enough*. Ambition is quashed as we strive to be loved and accepted. The castle shrinks into a two-bedroomed semi! But those stories aren't necessarily the truth. Those rooms are still there, ready to be opened up again and explored some more. Maybe it's true that you're not good at sport. We can't all be and maybe you don't even like sport but it doesn't make you wrong or a lesser person.

I think of stories that I carried with me and I honestly don't know where they came from. A couple stand out for me. The first was that academically I could never live up to my younger siblings and I know that one of the reasons or maybe the main one for doing my Open University degree was to prove myself. I understand now that because of my deep unhappiness at school I did not achieve and both my

O level and A level results were poor but not because I was not as clever as my siblings. The other story I told myself was that I was different from the rest of my family and that somehow that made me wrong. Through work I have done and continue to do with others, I know that I am different in lots of ways but I have learnt to value that difference rather than judge it.

In coaching we use various terms to describe this thinking; *self-limiting beliefs*, *gremlin* and I shall be using the word *saboteur* later in the book as we think about ways of managing it. Can you think of any stories that you carry with you? If not right now, start to notice them. There will be more help on this later in the book in chapter 3

Now I want you to think about your values. I hope that this book might be the start of your journey. On any journey it is a help to have a road map or a satnav and I hope that by discovering or clarifying your own values you can develop your own satnav. It's part of finding out where you are now.

Key Points of Chapter 1

- A focus on values and why they are so important if we are going to lead a fulfilling life
- How they may show up in the by giving you some examples from my childhood
- What they are, where they originate and their links to personality and spirituality
- How values are influenced by people around us
- How we can end up shutting away aspects of who we are in our desire to gain approval from those around us
- How we start to create stories about ourselves that have an impact on our lives
- How to clarify your values and how you are honouring them in your life at the moment

Moments to Ponder

I am going to share with you the exercise I do with my clients to help them develop a list of their values. Just write down the answers as they come

What makes your heart sing? ....
....
....
....
....

What makes you angry or drives you crazy? ....
....
....
....
....

Think of a moment in your life when life felt especially rewarding or poignant. Make sure you recall a particular scene rather than a phase in your life and answer these questions:

What was happening? ....
....
....
....

What was good about this? ....
....
....
....

What did it give you? ....
....
....
....

What made this a special and outstanding experience? We call this a peak moment ....
....
....
....

Think of the 3 people you most admire. They can be alive or dead and don't have to be famous. What is important is that you have enormous respect for them. List 4-8 qualities in each of those individuals . Once you've done that, write each word on a separate slip of paper and group the words together.

Person 1 ....

Qualities ....

....

....

Person 2 ....

Qualities ....

....

....

Person 3 ....

Qualities ....

....

....

Create word strings to represent each of your values (as I did earlier in the chapter for my value of freedom). This helps to make it clear what we mean by each word (value). For example, trustworthiness/confidentiality/reliability. See if you can do 10:

1 ....

2 ....

3 ....

4 ....

5 ....

6 ....

7 ....

8 ....

9 ....

10 ....

Consider how you are honouring the values in your life: score each value out of 10 and think of what small action you can take to increase that score. Complete the following table:

VALUE	SCORE	ACTION
....	....	....
....	....	....
....	....	....
....	....	....
....	....	....
....	....	....
....	....	....
....	....	....
....	....	....
....	....	....
....	....	....
....	....	....
....	....	....
....	....	....

Activity log

What is my learning from reading this chapter and working through the exercise? ....
....
....

What actions am I going to take as a result? ....
....
....

By when am I going to have done it/them? ....
....
....

What is the benefit of accomplishing this action? ....
....
....

What is the cost of not accomplishing this action? ....
....
....

Chapter 2

The world of work

How many people I wonder, fall into a career more by chance than making a conscious choice? There are real consequences to that which may include apathy at the very least, a lack of any real joy in work and at worst lead to stress and burn out. I have met many people who feel stuck in unfulfilling careers because of the pay, the status, the pension and at heart, the fear of change from something that, even if lacking enjoyment, meaning or purpose, gives a feeling of security. At least the bills will be paid. I was lucky, I loved what I did but there was a conflict of values, my own and that of the organisation I worked for: the NHS.

This chapter is about my career choice of nursing and what influenced my decision to go into that profession but I'm also taking a look at why nurses may choose that as a career. If you're not a nurse or you don't work in the NHS then you may wish to skip the first few paragraphs of this chapter. Or you may be curious, in which case read on. What I'm saying here doesn't necessarily pertain to just nursing but also to other helping professions. It may help you start to reflect on what influenced your career choice. Many women are carers in one way or another and some of what I'm saying in this chapter goes beyond a career in a helping profession and goes into our personal lives and how we manage the caring element of that. I'm also going to take the opportunity to look at nursing in the 21st century, as I feel nurses are getting a bad press at the moment. But I'm also going to challenge you to think about work, whatever you do, in a different way and maybe help you to start looking for your passion and what inspires you, by giving you a chance to discover your life purpose.

Why Did I Choose Nursing?

There was never any question about my decision to be a nurse. It was always what I was going to do for as long as I can remember. What influenced my decision? For a start, medicine was in my blood. Both my maternal grandfather and my uncle were GP's and I had a great-uncle who was a pioneering neurosurgeon at St Thomas's in London. That was the hospital to which I was encouraged to apply because of those family connections. However, even at that tender age, I did express my views and was very unhappy at the idea of being accepted somewhere because of people I knew rather than on my ability. That has remained with me in my views about positive discrimination. I strongly believe in being the best I can be and being accepted for that reason rather than any other.

The history of medical practice in my family goes way back. There is a story well known in my family of the family flight from France with the Huguenots in the seventeenth century. The father of this family, Laurens Roussel, remained in France under house arrest. He was an apothecary, a precursor to modern day doctors, and his name has lived on; Roussel is the name of my mother's cousin, my middle name and also the middle name of one of my nieces.

There were other influences, as I had allowed a book to affect my decision to go to boarding school, so it was a television programme that excited me about nursing. I can hardly remember it now but it was called *Emergency Ward 10*, a programme which had what we would now see as incredibly stereotypical views about doctors and nurses. Opportunities for women then, were far less than they are now. The choices seemed to be teaching, nursing, secretarial work or university for the really brainy girls in the school. Career choice for women has changed beyond all recognition since I left school and there are many jobs/roles/careers that weren't even invented then, for example, what I do now, coaching.

I never even considered going to university. I had created a story that I was not clever enough to do that but also I did have a genuine desire to train as a nurse. I also have to say that once my teachers knew I wanted to be a nurse, they didn't take much interest in me. I suppose medicine could have been an option but there weren't that many female doctors then, and despite the thinking by the medical profession and society, and possibly nurses themselves, I have never seen nursing as being something inferior to medicine. I see it as being complimentary and of equal value and importance but I do wonder if that is why so many girls now choose medicine over nursing. Is it seen as somehow better? However, for me nursing was truly a vocation and I loved it.

When my sister was born, I loved to look after her and I used to take her out a lot. I well remember the looks I received, the teenager pushing a toddler around in her push chair. Teenage motherhood was most definitely frowned upon in the sixties! This must have brought out the caring and compassionate side of my personality and so it was no surprise when I chose children's nursing as my career and ultimately ended up at Great Ormond Street on the combined children's and adults' nurse training.

Nursing Then and Now

There were many things I remember about my training that make me question current methods of doing things. I don't think I ever stopped, and, at the end of my nursing career it was probably my downfall, challenging the way things were done and the culture within which patient care took place. I was always striving to deliver better care and also better care for nurses themselves. I remain passionate about the profession despite my decision to leave. When I think of the NHS, I am reminded of the metaphors; *the insatiable swallower* and the *blazing red glutton* in *Tess of the D'Urbervilles,* used by Thomas Hardy to describe the threshing machine that Tess is constantly feeding. There never seems any end to the demands of that machine. My later experiences of the NHS were the same and I only see those demands increasing.

However, when I started my training it was busy.We worked hard but I have no recollection of it being like it appears to be now. Having watched a recent television programme, *Casualty 1909*, depicting the nursing profession in the 1900's, the world I entered in 1969 was more like that than it appears to be now. There was a matron in charge, Miss Kirby was her name and she was respected by everyone. The hospital ran like clockwork and the work always got done. We all knew our tasks and basic nursing care was all important. In more recent years we have had debates such as 'too posh to wash' about nurses who are apparently reluctant to bath their patients and the nursing innovation first published in 2001, *Essence of Care.* This was written in an attempt to bring back what is now called the fundamentals of nursing care, but which, for me, is what nursing is about: delivering holistic care and addressing the physical, emotional and spiritual needs of the individual patient. I remember in my year as a staff nurse on a paediatric neurosurgical ward, the difference real nursing care made to very sick children.

However, I must not look back with rose-tinted spectacles. It was far from all good. At that time, there were fixed visiting hours so that children were without their parents for long periods. I well remember the time when I thought I would sit on a child's bed and play with him when I heard the roar of the ward sister, they were real harridans, "*Nurse Hamilton (my maiden name), haven't you got cupboards to clean?*" Nor was any kind of emotional involvement with patients and their families allowed and yet this was a hospital where the sickest of children were cared for and where many of them died.

There is a fascinating research paper published back in 1960 [1] about the defence mechanisms put up by nurses to protect themselves from the intense feelings of fear, guilt and anxiety brought up in them when faced with illness and vulnerability. It has been suggested [2] that this seminal work has resulted in significant change in the profession. I would challenge that. Yes, change has happened but has it been fully embraced by the profession? If we take clinical supervision, the opportunity that should be taken by all registered nurses to reflect on their practice and receive the support necessary to deliver high quality care, then I think not. I believe that only a small percentage of nurses take part in that, citing many reasons time, in particular for not doing it. Having worked in that field for many years now, I believe that to be unacceptable. I see even now a culture in nursing which does not embrace self-care. Nor do I see the profession appreciating that if they truly wish to make a difference to patients in a holistic way that they need to care for themselves first. Neither do I see employers wishing to support them in developing that self-care. I am aware that this may come over as a bit of a rant but it is because of the concern I feel for the wellbeing of nurses.

Suffice it to say, I well remember the evening when my ward sister colleague and I had to switch off the ventilator of a 13-year old boy who consequently died. Our response was to buy a packet of cigarettes and some wine, which we proceeded to consume back at her flat. That was how we coped. However, this culture and this behaviour is significant when I look at how I dealt with the life events I was going to be faced with in the future. It reinforced for me a developing pattern of behaviour which has not served me and that was to not ask for help when I needed it.

For example, the first real love of my life was a doctor but a married doctor. He introduced me to opera. On our first date we went to a performance of Verdi's *Force of Destiny*. I was bowled over by him and by opera which I have loved ever since. There followed a short and sweet romance which came to an end at the Christmas of that year. I did not manage that loss well, especially as in the January of the following year my grandfather had a stroke and died. Apart from the loss of animals, this was my first real encounter with grief and here were two intense losses within only a few weeks of each other. It was probably the first time in my life that I did not share my grief but kept it to myself. After all look at what I was seeing in my work; the overwhelming grief that a parent experiences at the loss of their child. Somehow my grief did not seem worthy. I'm not sure how I got through that time, it's a long time ago but I do remember taking a mixture of valium and vodka with no real intention of ending my life, but it was a bizarre cry for help. No one ever knew. We all manage grief in different ways and I will return to this in chapters 4 and 8.

I continued children's nursing for another year, after which I thought I would go to college to study for health visiting. I had no idea what health visiting was but I liked the idea of no more shift working and better money. By this time I was well established in London and was having fun, so anything that supported that seemed like a good idea. Also, I did enjoy it, and it has influenced the direction my career has taken, both directly and indirectly, as you will see in later chapters of the book.

Getting Married

One of the things work allows us to do is go on holiday! A year after I completed my health visiting training I went on holiday, with a friend, to the Greek island of Mykonos. Sitting behind us on the plane were 3 rather loud young men! The trip to Mykonos then did not just involve a plane, it also involved a ferry from Piraeus. Imagine my surprise when one of these men offered to carry my suitcase off the boat and promptly joined the bus taking us to our destination. Imagine my surprise too when I walked on to the balcony of our room and he walked onto the same balcony from the room next door. That was the beginning of a holiday romance, a holiday romance that worked. A year later we got married and at the time of writing we have just passed our 33rd wedding anniversary! My verdict on those years? Iain has been a brilliant husband, incredibly supportive of everything that I have done and I love him to bits!

Why Choose the Helping Professions?

So what makes nurses choose to go into the profession? Indeed why do people choose the *helping professions*? I have already looked at my reasons including my choice to go into nursing rather than medicine but now I want to focus on why any of us might choose a helping profession; by that, as well as nursing, I mean medicine, teaching, social work, law (particularly family law) or any career where we help people in some way or another.

We need to explore all our motives [3], not just the altruistic ones, which take us there. We may have a hidden need for power, both in being with people who seem worse off than ourselves in some way or that we can take charge of the lives of the people we work with. It's worth all of us being brave enough to reflect on I think! Sometimes clinging to the role of helper makes it difficult to see both the strengths in our patients/clients and the vulnerability in ourselves. In fact, I wrote an article myself on just such an issue [4] in which I put forward my belief that, as health visitors in this case, we resist owning our own vulnerability and thus project it onto our clients making them 'needy' in some way. When I was doing my research for my masters' degree, I remember reading a book [5] whose authors discovered that in addition to all of the above, nurses tended to have low self-esteem and care for others more than they care for themselves. So where was I in all of this? Actually, I can see me in all of it!

A couple of things happened that have completely changed my view of all of this, apart from my time in therapy and my ongoing coaching and supervision. The first thing was when I was being encouraged to take sick leave in 2000 when my stress symptoms were becoming obvious. My response to my director of nursing was that I couldn't possibly go off sick. Three of *my mums* who I had been working quite intensively with were due to have their babies and needed me. I look back at that with a degree of shame at the sheer arrogance of it which is reflected in the following words: "*Much is done in the name of service. Some is not so helpful; some is even arrogance disguised as help for others*" [6, p55].

Anyway, I went off sick and those women were visited by another health visitor in my absence and of course, were fine. A salutary tale for myself and others who feel themselves to be indispensable. As the coactive coaching model tells me, *our clients are all naturally creative, resourceful and whole* [7]. By that, I mean nothing needs fixing. We all have the resources we need within us to give us the answers and help that we require. I really saw this idea at work when I was doing a workshop recently with a group of mental health service users. One of the participants had quite a profound border line personality disorder. I had been taught that there was nothing you could do with a patient

with that condition, so I was really anxious about
would go. What was so humbling to see was the way
participated in the session and really got something
seeing that part of herself: the fun-loving spontanec
indeed naturally creative, resourceful and whole.

Nursing in the 21st Century

It's here that I want to comment on nursing and health visiting in the
21st century because I feel that these dedicated professionals are really
getting a bad press. Whereas I do feel that they could be standing up
for themselves, I would like, in some way, to put the record straight
for those on the front line. However, I should point out that anything
I write here is my opinion! Despite successive governments assuring
us that they were committing millions of pounds of taxpayers' money
to the NHS, it never seems to reach front line services. Nurses and
health visitors I have met over the last few years feel stressed, put
down, undervalued and lacking in motivation. Leadership has been
poor and micromanagement is in the ascendancy. Where leadership
is good, patient care improves. In addition, I have met many nurses
who have left the NHS and others who are choosing to take early
retirement. What a waste! If I could make a difference it would be
to help nurses move from being victims of the system to taking
responsibility for themselves and their own health and well-being.

Attitudes to Work

Anyway, it's time to move the focus away from me to you. First let's
think about the stories concerning work that we have grown up with.
We talk about 'work/life balance' as though somehow the two are
separate. Isn't work a part of life? And if it is such a large part of life
then surely we should enjoy it. Or should we buy into the protestant
work ethic that says work is only work if it's hard and that we have to
suffer and go through a process of survival until we get our pension.
We can only be successful if we work really hard and for long hours.
It all seems to be about suffering and something we have to do in
exchange for money. What if it doesn't have to be like that? I have
been inspired by Nick Williams [8] to see work in a new way, a *work
ethic of joy*, [Nick's words]. He quotes Kalil Galbrain who says that
"Your work is your love made visible".

We are all going to have to work far longer now, so why don't we
adopt that work ethic of joy and find work that inspires us and that
we can feel passionate about? In the 21st century there is definitely a

ove towards discovering what nourishes our soul. That must include our work otherwise we are left with an emptiness inside, a sense of a lack of fulfilment or at worst we can experience stress or burnout. We need to consider our personal values because if they are at odds with the values of the organisation that we work for, then we are in trouble. Nursing and health visiting certainly encompass my values and I was passionate about the work and remember feeling that I would happily stay in that role until I retired. But I began to realise that my values were not shared by the organisation who employed me. As I worked my notice I remember this thought popping into my head *They have stifled my creativity*; creativity is another of my values and by that, I mean space to look at things differently, to find new ways of doing things. At that time I was unaware of the importance of values but now that I am, I really understand what that thought represented.

Many of us fail to bring into the world all the *music* and potential we hold inside. Many of us simply accept our working life the way it is. We feel stuck with little or no choice. We will return to choice and how we can make conscious powerful choices in chapter 7. Apart from the way we think about work, what stops us having inspiring work that we feel passionate about and why does it matter? Because when you do work you feel passionate about, you just flow and as long as you manage your energy then the whole work/life balance thing is not an issue. But something stops us taking that big step; there's a real resistance to taking the true direction of our lives [9]. As I've already alluded to, we create stories as we grow up and these in turn become the voice of our saboteur [7]. The voice in our heads making suggestions such as *What makes you think you can do that? How do you think you are going to pay your mortgage, your bills, university fees et cetera? You ought to stay in that safe career, it's a job for life.* Need I go on! The saboteur or my saboteur will return in later chapters and I will be giving you some simple and fun techniques to manage it in the next chapter.

I sacrificed the pension for my health and now, I see, for a life of fulfilment. My income took a complete nosedive in 2009 but it was one of the most powerful lessons I have ever learnt. It was OK, we survived, even though at times we weren't sure how we were going to pay the bills. We made several choices that included not having a holiday and it didn't matter because of that sense of real fulfilment and excitement that I was experiencing about my work and still am.

But there is more to it than that. Are we afraid of our potential greatness? of what we could be if we did play to our full potential [9].

Quite a thought isn't it? It's back to the saboteur again who also has the power to keep us small and not let our true selves be seen [10]. We live in a perfectionist world and are afraid that if we let ourselves be seen, that we would be perceived as less than perfect. To follow the route of our true self, we need to not be afraid of being vulnerable.

So many of us just don't want to show up in the world, particularly women. Less than a hundred years since women gained the vote in this country, just look at how few women are in positions of power in this country. At the time of writing, there is just about to be a Labour Party leadership election in this country. Four white, male, 40 somethings to join the other two (David Cameron and Nick Clegg white, male and 40 something and already at the heart of British Government) and one black female. In my heart, I can't help but wonder if her entry into the election is being taken seriously.

So let me share this quote from Brene Brown with you and I just want you to think about it before you begin to consider the questions I am going to ask you to conclude this chapter.

"Owning our own story can be hard but not nearly as difficult as spending our lives running from it. Embracing our vulnerabilities is risky but not nearly as dangerous as giving up on love and belonging and joy – the experiences that make us the most vulnerable. Only when we are brave enough to explore the darkness will we discover the infinite power of our light" [10, p6].

Key Points of Chapter 2

- The factors that can affect our choice of career
- A spotlight on nursing and the changes over the last 40 years
- Some reasons why we choose to go into the helping professions
- Attitudes to work
- What gets in the way of choosing a career path of inspiration/joy
- An opportunity for you to look at your career and life purpose

Moments to Ponder

What influenced/motivated you in your choice of career? ....

....

....

....

....

How do you rate your current level of job satisfaction out of 10? (10 being amazing, zero being dreadful) ....

....

....

....

....

How do the values of your organisation match your own? And how does that feel? ....

....

....

....

....

Please don't worry if you struggle with any of the exercises in the book. Even if it opens your eyes a bit to what might be possible and then you choose to go and work with a coach to find out more then that's great. (More about coaching in chapters 8 and 9.)

The last exercise I am asking you to do here is called life purpose: by life purpose I mean what you are here (in the world) to do. It's not just about your career either, it's about how you live your life. Clarity about your life purpose will help you see if you're on the right path:

Think back in your life to a time when you were fully alive and felt strong and powerful. What were you doing? Who were you with? What was happening around you? What was your impact? ....

....

....

....

....

....

Imagine yourself at a ripe old age, sitting on a porch in a rocking chair. Friends surround you and are telling stories and speaking of the difference you have made in their lives. What do they say? ....

....

....

....

Just journal about your learning from this exercise and see if you can put into words what you feel your life purpose to be. The bottom line of this question is a powerful one, what are you here in this world to do? Quite a big question and one, I bet, you haven't thought about before. It is one I have only been considering in the past few years and has contributed to the changes I have made in my career.

Activity log

What is my learning from reading this chapter and working through the exercise? ....

....

....

....

What actions am I going to take as a result? ....

....

....

....

By when am I going to have done it/them? ....

....

....

....

What is the benefit of accomplishing this action? ....

....

....

....

What is the cost of not accomplishing this action? ....

....

....

....

Chapter 3

Becoming a mother

Aren't we meant to believe that having a baby is the pinnacle, the most joyous occasion of a woman's life, something we have planned and longed for? And indeed it is! It is rare to meet a woman who wished they'd never become a mum, but is that the whole of the experience? Isn't there a time when you realize that your ordered life has been irrevocably turned upside down by this little scrap of humanity? At times it can make you feel out of control, run ragged or inadequate, guilty or sad. Then you wonder who was that woman who was in charge of a class, managed a team in some organization, or led a service in the public sector? How different now than many years ago in my mother's generation when the challenge was to prevent conception, not plan your babies like clockwork as you plan the rest of your life.

In this chapter, I want to bust some of the myths around motherhood and look at my experience of becoming a mother: the conception, the delivery, bonding, breast feeding, sadness and loss. It's a key part of my own journey and I see those middle years between the ages of 30 and 50 as having enormous significance to what has happened since. I also see those years as being a time of transition for many women who take the opportunity to make significant choices about their career either in those early years of having a family or when their children flee the nest. The key point I want to make is that this time of great joy is also a time of immense change and therein lies a paradox; change can mirror loss and many of the emotions we experience at that time are associated with that change and with the losses we experience through that change. These emotions can include a perfectly normal and understandable low mood and sadness for what we have lost but that does not necessarily mean that we have the clinical illness of postnatal depression. My story happened 30 years ago and society's views have changed since then along with our expectations. With that has come new research, new ideas and my professional career and my passion for this area has given me an opportunity to reflect on my own experience and I can now share some of my learning.

I will also introduce you to your *saboteur* [1], otherwise known as the *gremlin* [2], the *chatterbox* [3], the *censor* [4]. You may also know the more technical term *self-limiting beliefs*. I list all these different names because it shows what an important concept this is and the power this little beastie can hold over us. But more about that later.

Motherhood

I waited 7 long months to conceive and at the early stages of pregnancy I hardly dared believe it was true. I hate to admit it now but I smoked until I actually saw the baby move inside me and then immediately stopped. It was true! I was pregnant! And then I really blossomed. I loved it, I felt very special in the way pregnant women do but at 36 weeks I was given what was for me the most devastating news, that I was to have a Caesarian section. The obstetrician who scanned me (scanning was in its early days then) confirmed what he had suspected that my baby was breech and he recommended a Caesarean section under general anaesthetic. It was the very early days of epidurals and he was an old school obstetrician. Also, my own view was that if I was going to have this done then they would have to knock me out anyway!

What took me by surprise was my reaction to that news. I can still picture me now almost 30 years later walking through the streets of the town where I lived in tears. This wasn't what I planned. This was in no way the way I wanted to start my child's life. I had no misconceptions about childbirth, after all I was working with women who often described their experiences in graphic detail but I wanted to join women in that experience, after all it was part of being a woman. As I write this now I am aware that part of this loss was about not joining motherhood in the true way, not being a real woman, failing in some way. It still is a great sadness to me that I never did experience the pain, the exhilaration of delivering my child and, yes, I know many women think I'm mad but that's just how it was for me!

I have always been curious as to whether the sudden decision by the obstetrician to deliver Laura by Caesarian section was in any way linked to my symptoms of postnatal depression. So I started to look for a link but there appears to be no direct connection [5] and in the field of postnatal depression where there are so many risk factors involved maybe that is not surprising. However, there are studies that link Caesarian sections to feelings of grief and loss and low self esteem [6, 7]. It is also possible [7] that the impact may be less where the mother has an epidural and has a partner or supportive person with her, which of course is often the case now but not then.

So I went into the hospital on 26 November 1980. I was so organised, everything was ready for Christmas and the freezer was fully stocked but this was not how I wanted it to have been. Instead, the excited anticipation was replaced by fear, a fear that I would not survive the operation to experience motherhood and another real fear that the baby they gave me would not be mine.

Around lunchtime on the 27th I was wheeled down to theatre. Where was Iain at the time? I think he was with me but I can't remember. What did he feel? Fear I think too but I must ask him. I know he waited in a side room and as I write this with tears in my eyes I wonder if he experienced some of this loss too. The joy of this occasion which was to be our only chance was cruelly taken away. Neither of us would witness the birth of our child.

Then there was the blackness of the anaesthetic and the next thing I can remember was fighting my way out of a black hole, screaming, screaming. I was fighting to survive, I had to live to see my baby. But this was some kind of a nightmare, a reaction, maybe, to the anaesthetic, and of course I survived. They took me back to the ward and as I woke there was my baby in an incubator all dressed up. Another fear: what was wrong with her? Incubators were for sick or premature babies, not healthy ones. But she was cold, that was all – what a relief. Was she mine I wondered? When they took off her hat and I was able to hold her I knew in my heart she was mine. She reminded me of a photo of another baby with a mass of dark curly hair reminiscent of a toilet brush! ME! So that was OK. Now the next fear: I knew that the sooner the baby was put to the breast the more likely was breastfeeding to be successful. I never anticipated feeding her any other way. I had to get her to the breast. I was still very woozy from the anaesthetic but I do remember between myself, Iain and a lovely nursery nurse who I had worked with in the community but whose name I have now forgotten, Laura was put to the breast and thankfully fed. Yes I got that bit right!

In view of what was to follow that was a good thing. It is possible that breastfeeding may provide emotional benefit to depressed mothers. To quote Brooke Shields [8]: "*Breastfeeding was my only real connection to the baby. If I were to eliminate that I might have no hope of coming through this nightmare*" [p80]. She had found herself under pressure to give up breastfeeding by well meaning friends and relatives as it was felt that that would help her recover from her depression. For some of us breastfeeding is exactly the right thing to do, we want to do it, it feels right and it helps us to feel close to our babies. For other women it is completely different; they feel pressurized into doing something that they hate or struggle with, they lose sleep and, at worst, it can contribute to a spiral down into depression. Most of us know that breast is best, as the saying goes, but in my view, the relationship between mother and baby is far more crucial to the baby's future health and wellbeing than feeding. I struggle with the near evangelistic culture that has developed over the years which puts mothers under unnecessary pressure to breast feed. The love between mother and baby and that bond is immeasurably more important.

Then followed the days in hospital but I can't remember too much about that. In those days you stayed in 10 days after a section. I do remember my determination to stand up straight, unlike so many women I had seen who walked around bent after surgery and I remain convinced that that aided my recovery. I also think that being in hospital getting to know Laura and feeling comfortable about feeding her was really important. I felt safe there. I haven't mentioned bonding, that intense experience described by so many women did not happen for me. There was nothing. Another loss and because of the wound from surgery, I was unable to pick her up when she cried and I had to wait for a nurse to come and pick her up for me.

There is some recent research concluding that Caesarian section may prevent the release of the hormone oxytocin which is linked to feelings of love [9]. It is at its highest in the moments after birth giving a woman those feelings of falling in love with her baby but we also know that, as with any form of love, it can take time to develop and it did. I have never doubted my feelings for my daughter even when things were pretty dark when she was a baby and later as a teenager. A mother's love for her child is truly unconditional.

I have a memory of a baby smiling at me. I didn't believe it was possible then but I was convinced at the time that that was what I had seen. It used to be thought that a tiny baby's smile was wind but it is now thought that these smiles which may be as fleeting as seeing a softening or brightening of the baby's expression [10] are indeed smiles. Newborn babies are far more amazing than we think in their ability to communicate a range of emotions [11].

Coming Home

The great day arrived when I could take my baby home, the beginning of the next part of my life, such an important part, the part so many women, so many couples long for. My mum was there for that first week which helped make it all feel so easy. Then she went home. I still remember that first evening at home, Laura cried and cried, and I just didn't know what to do. Iain held her until she fell asleep on him and that was to be the pattern for evening after evening. We would do everything we could but nothing would stop that incessant screaming. Eventually, I imagine she was so exhausted she fell asleep and we would put her to bed and finally have some peace until she woke again. In fact, I would always wake before she did and I have since read somewhere that that is often the case with depressed mothers. This very difficult time started with my mother's visit and ended with my visiting my parents three months later. A coincidence? I don't think so. I can only imagine that it was something to do with me having the support I needed. It is commonly believed that infant colic is the cause of this crying but both as a mother and a professional I think that this intense crying in the early weeks of a baby's life is much more complex than that.

She slept from the beginning in her own room. Was that right? I don't know. I had the feeling that it was but we now know that room sharing lessens the incidence of cot death. But I also desperately wanted her to be independent and, as I look back, I did find it difficult to be close to her. I still have a vivid image of myself in our sitting room and her in her pram on the other side of the room with what seemed like an unfathomable gap between us. However, I do have other memories, fun memories. For example, dancing around the room with her at the age of about 6 months and the Abba song *Waterloo* is playing! Since then there has been a growing infant massage movement and we are learning what a difference it can make to mothers and their babies [12].

I was alone, desperately alone. Yes, I had and still have a wonderful husband who wanted to be far more involved but when it came to bringing up our daughter, I had to do it myself. After all, I was the expert wasn't I? The health visitor clearly thought so. She walked into our house and said in so many words that as I was a health visitor I obviously knew what I was doing. She never came to my house again. I went to the clinic week after week but she never spoke to me and never asked how Laura or I were. How many women long to be asked how they are in a genuine empathic way so that they can say how they really feel?

I created my own aloneness. I never asked for help. I never wanted anyone to know how useless I was. I had no family nearby and no close friends. I remember one other mum I had met in ante-natal class: we used to go round to each others' houses to have coffee and for our babies to play together. Then the competitive element crept in. Her baby was always doing more than mine which of course created more evidence that I was a useless mother but one thing she did do was suggest I used a dummy which I did and that made so much difference! However, our friendship cooled and I had very few other friends in the area. We had only moved there 2 years previously and until I went on maternity leave, I had been working full time, and our friends at that time tended to be from other parts of the country.

That time was one of loneliness and aloneness, the days during which I cried and she cried, the nights of trying to get her back to sleep. However, once she learnt to suck her pink blanket, the remains of which left with her when she left home, things slowly began to improve and we both cried less.

It was also a time of very harsh self-judgment. Whatever I did was never good enough. I remember when I started her on solids: that was exciting. Maybe she would depend less on me? But of course I had do it properly: I had to give her family food. The first time, I cooked her fish, potatoes and peas and spent hours blending it only for her to spit it out. She had lovely Beatrix Potter dishes given to her as Christening presents and every one got broken as I hurled them across the room in my anger. I now know that those outbursts of anger or aggression usually directed at Iain or Laura over the next few years were because of my poor emotional and mental health. Since I have been in therapy and coaching, those outbursts are virtually non-existent.

When Laura was six months old I went back to work for two days a week. That was probably the best thing that could have happened for both of us. I had some social contact and intellectual stimulation and was doing a job I enjoyed. Laura went to a childminder where she was really happy and had the company of other children which she has always loved. As I look back now, I wonder if that was part of the problem. My aloneness was her aloneness too.

Mild to Moderate Postnatal Depression: a response to change and loss?

It wasn't until years later and when I learnt about post-natal depression, that I realised what had been going on for me but there was no one there to recognise it at the time and of course I would always put on a brave front and say that everything was fine and I did not ask for help.

I have long believed that many of the feelings we share from a range of life events are about loss and that's where we can understand each other even when our individual experiences are different. Some degree of grief is a normal response to any loss and with any major life change there is loss. The associated feelings of anxiety, happiness, fear, threat, guilt and depression through to gradual acceptance and moving forward, are normal and natural. It's only now I can see it for what it is, that I have been able to accept my feelings and let go of the guilt associated with them. I love being British and I'm proud of it. I think that we live in a beautiful country but I wish we could get our act together when it comes to feelings and emotions and try not to maintain the stiff upper lip attitude. It doesn't serve us and it didn't serve me. We must challenge the stigma that is rife in our society.

I was fascinated to read that a paradox of loss and joy in motherhood has been identified through research [13]. For me, and my experience of working with other mothers tells me I am not alone, the joy and happiness I experienced in the birth of my daughter was indeed tainted with loss. There was the loss of the anticipated delivery, the loss of that feeling of falling in love with my baby and, indeed, there was a loss of a fantasy of how I would be as a mother. A recent comment made by my husband was that having a baby *clipped my wings*. I lost the freedom that I have always held so dear and it is these experiences, both personal and professional, that convince me that so much of the low mood felt by women after childbirth is deep sadness at a range of losses. These may include loss of sleep, loss of money, loss of independence, loss of old patterns of relationship, sexuality; the list is in fact endless. Therefore, what we experience is not necessarily abnormal.

It is important to acknowledge the grief that these losses bring and allow ourselves to experience a healthy grief reaction which would enable us to accept what we have lost. So in writing this chapter, I really want to challenge the medicalisation of a condition which so many women suffer from. It should not be ignored, nor brushed under the carpet, nor should women be made to feel guilty or inadequate for having these feelings but instead be supported in a way which is empowering for them while they go through this time. We should be normalizing this process and not pathologising it but without some kind of supportive intervention, a woman can find herself alone and spiralling down into a deeper depression which may have a longer term impact on the mother, the new baby [14] and the family as a whole. A trustworthy, compassionate listening ear may be all that it takes to make a difference but equally it is important to take some responsibility to help ourselves by telling someone how we are feeling. That's what I didn't do.

We're not blank canvases when we become mothers. We have a history, we have our dreams and aspirations, our values and our ways of dealing with things and our stories. I never dreamed that I would have any difficulties being a mum. I made up somewhere along the line that I was born to be a mother, that I would have a large family but what a surprise the next few years were going to bring. On top of that was what I brought into motherhood in terms of the way I coped: I was a nurse and nurses always cope; they never ask for help. And there is not a *type* of woman who *gets* depression. There are so many factors that can contribute to it. Typically we read about single mothers living in poverty, unemployment, substance abuse and childhood abuse but there are another group of women who may choose to have their babies later in life or who may have assisted conception, whose expectations are enormously high. These women too, are at risk. There are factors in our biology, our psychology and our social world that can contribute [15] to the way we handle motherhood.

Over the years I have read vast quantities of literature on the subject, particularly in my role as a health professional and I kept coming across the same old statistic: 10-15% of women experience depression and a few (1-2 women per 1000) go on to develop the serious clinical illness puerperal psychosis. However, the figures are startlingly different in Paula Nicolson's study [13]. She estimates that 70% of new mothers experience depressed moods, feeling significantly *low* or *down* over the first year of their baby's life. Her figures seem to back up my argument.

Whatever the extent of the *illness* or *experience*, it is important to identify it early so that appropriate help and support can be given to prevent further deterioration in the woman's mental health, recurrence of depression later on and the potential impact on the baby and other family members. What happened for me was the mild end of the spectrum. Nevertheless, no one asked me how I was, no one knew and so no help or support was available.

Meet your Saboteur

I have talked a lot about the feelings that beset us as new mothers and one of those is the way we can judge ourselves so harshly. Therefore, it feels like the right time to meet your saboteur and to start hearing its voice. It's a voice of shoulds and oughts and judgments and beliefs that we have built up over the years, and for us have become the hard truth. They have real impact on our feelings and our behaviour and make us feel and play small. They tend to be very powerful around our perceptions of ourselves as a mother, which is why I introduce it here. The saboteur gets very noisy at times of change and therein may lie the reason for its presence in the new world of motherhood. However, it's always around throughout your life.

Key Points of Chapter 3

- The transition to parenthood is a major life change
- Various factors have an impact on how we adjust for example, method of delivery
- Low mood after birth may be due to major life change and associated losses
- Get to know your saboteur because the beliefs we hold limit us and have an impact on our feelings and behaviour
- Having a feel-good list will help us when we are having a difficult time

Moments to Ponder

The more you hear a judgmental voice with words like *should, ought,* et cetera and see it as your saboteur, the less the potential it has to harm you. If you are hearing your saboteur then I'm going to give you a couple of simple strategies to challenge it.

Sit somewhere comfortable and dream, reflect, think and notice what your saboteur is saying. I'm guessing that this is something that you don't normally do so, I think it will have quite a lot to say!

Have a bit of fun and strike up a dialogue with him/her. Give your saboteur a job to do, a place to go or even a holiday to go on. This may sound whacky but it works. I've done it and my clients do it. They start to notice their saboteur and it does far less harm!

Here's a tip I have gained from my dear friend and colleague, Elaine Hanzak-Gott [16]: start to create a feel-good list which you keep to hand for those days when you're not feeling so good, when your saboteur is having a field day and keep it in a place where you can always find it when you need it. You know those smells, those sounds, those sights that just make you feel fantastic, write them down, anything that really appeals to your senses (sight, hearing, smell, taste and touch) and keep adding to them. Then, when you have a down time, look at those lists and just take a few moments out to listen to that piece of music, to look at those pictures or to smell that rose. You will feel better. When you're really in the moment with feeling good, the saboteur is powerless!

Feel-good list: ....

....

....

....

....

....

....

....

....

....

....

....
....
....
....
....
....
....
....
....
....
....
....
....
....
....

Activity log

What is my learning from reading this chapter and working through the exercise? ....
....
....

What actions am I going to take as a result? ....
....
....
....

By when am I going to have done it/them? ....
....
....
....

What is the benefit of accomplishing this action? ....
....
....
....

What is the cost of not accomplishing this action? ....
....
....
....

Chapter 4

Wanting another baby

How many women are there like me who have experienced the longing for more children and it not happening or the real grief when you lose a longed for baby by miscarriage? Or maybe, as in my case, have experienced both and then feel we must just get on with our lives? It is only through researching both of these events that I have come to realise just how overwhelming those experiences were and the enormity of the impact of it on the next few years of my life.

This chapter describes that period of my life and I share some of what I've learnt through my reading about secondary infertility and miscarriage and the associated feelings. Feelings and emotions are not something we are good at in our culture but the more we can be with our feelings the less we will fear them. Emotional pain should be seen as a signal from our bodies telling us to take action in the same way as physical pain and we ignore it at our peril. It is my intention in this chapter to briefly address what may be seen as the rather controversial or alternatively 'touchy-feely' area of feelings and emotions and to challenge you to start to get familiar with them. I now know that ignoring what my body was telling me led to the mental illness I experienced some years later. I will also focus on grief and loss, as I know that many people will identify with the overwhelming intensity of that feeling.

Some Normality

Life settled down for me at work and for Laura at the childminders and we began to enjoy the days we had together. I remember as she learnt to walk, our journey to the village being slow with her but it was enjoyable and I became much more contented. Soon our house outgrew us and we moved up to Cambridge, a bit further north from our home near Bishops Stortford. I gave up work, intending to return at a later date.

The day we moved to Cambridge was a hot one but a happy one too. I remember Laura running round the garden exploring all the little nooks and crannies with the intense curiosity that is so unique to a small child. It was then that she started to talk. The day after our move she looked out of the window, saw a cat and said *dog*. She never looked back!

Discovering how Difficult it was to Conceive

When Laura was about a year old, we decided we wanted to have another baby. It had taken a while for her to be conceived so we didn't feel it was too early. The months went by and nothing. That was so hard. The streets were full of pregnant women and mothers pushing their babies. My friends all had their 2 or 3 children and I remember the anger and resentment I felt at my sister-in-law and my best friend both expecting their second children. I found it hard even to talk to them. I was angry with people who couldn't wait for their children to be at school and off their hands. It seemed so unfair.

Eventually I went to see my doctor who referred me to the hospital. She seemed reluctant and I'm not really surprised. Going through all those investigations is undignified to say the least for both the man and the woman. It didn't do our sex life any favours either. I had to complete that temperature chart every night and a slight rise denoted ovulation showing us that tonight was the night, however tired and not in the mood we may have been feeling. An end to spontaneity! I also embarked on some hormone treatment, which involved frequent visits to the hospital for scans on specific days in my menstrual cycle. After a range of investigations and treatment, no underlying reason was found for our failure to conceive. IVF was put forward as a possibility, although very much in its infancy at that time, but after a couple of years we both decided that enough was enough and we wanted to move on with our lives. At least we had Laura and we wanted to enjoy her rather than miss her growing up as we saw each month go by in disappointment. I decided to push for one more test and then call it a day. Imagine how I felt when I arrived at outpatients for the results of that test to be kept waiting longer than ever. When I enquired I was informed that my records had been lost. I was incandescent with rage and had to be calmed down. There seemed to be no understanding of the emotional impact of the diagnosis, or rather lack of diagnosis, and the treatment.

On challenging the consultant about the apparent lack of emotional support, I was shocked but maybe not surprised to discover that this was not seen in any way as a priority. I vowed to set up a support group for women experiencing secondary infertility. I suppose we were a special group of women and I remember that sense of guilt for going through that emotional pain when I did at least have one child. What must it have been like to have never had one? I can only begin to imagine but I so wanted to have another one. Maybe then I could deliver normally and maybe have another go at being a mother and maybe do it better.

So I set up the group and it ran for a short while but when I decided I wanted to move on with my life, I knew that I had to leave the group behind as well. I often wonder if it ever led to anything bigger; it was certainly very much in its infancy and received no support from the NHS, who at the time showed no interest in what we were doing.

Moving On

At the time I started working as a child minder. At least that way I could be at home with Laura and earn some money to contribute to the family income. I did enjoy it and at least then there were no Ofsted inspections and targets so I was able to enjoy the children in my care, which most of the time I did. It was when Laura started school that I decided I wanted to stop and not have other people's children putting fingermarks everywhere! Also, Laura became incredibly jealous and I felt that in the time we were at home together, she should have my undivided attention.

I decided to go back to nursing and successfully applied for a job as a practice nurse. The hours were very flexible, which was just as well as I had only been in post for a day or so when Laura developed chicken pox! It suited us and most of the time we could fit our hours around Laura's school hours. Also, there was help from friends which I was able to reciprocate and I started studying for a degree with the Open University. I wasn't entirely sure that nursing was what I wanted to do for the rest of my life. I hoped that doing the degree would open up other possibilities. At a deeper level, I think that I also wanted to prove to myself and my family that I could achieve academically in the same way as my brother and sister had. What surprised me was that I found real fulfillment in undertaking the Arts degree and most of all enjoyed discovering that I could do it! This sense of fulfillment was reignited again some 10 years later when I undertook my master's degree. What was it like studying with a young, chatty and at times demanding child in the house? I remember attempting to shut myself away to study but found that impossible as there were constant interruptions. So I gave in and sat in the middle of the house at the dining room table; surprisingly much more peaceful. An approach I have recommended to others since!

Pregnant Again

Once again life settled down into some kind of routine and then 1987 arrived. My beloved grandmother was very ill and dying. I wanted to see her and was going to go up to Scotland with my mother to see her but the weather was appalling and I was very anxious about travelling so I decided not to go. It was a decision I will always regret because I was never able to say goodbye to her. My mother was relieved that at least I would remember her in the way she had lived most of her life, rather than seeing a sick and dying woman. Maybe she was right. And she died but I don't remember the date.

However, I was determined to get to her funeral. The day of the funeral dawned, it was foggy and we were flying to Edinburgh. We arrived at Stansted to find the flight was delayed. Had we waited we would never have made it to the funeral, so we did a dash round to Heathrow (I don't think the M25 was there then) and just got a flight that would get us there in time. Coincidentally, it was the same flight as my sister. I had to beg them to keep the embarkation gates open for us while Iain parked the car. Somehow my desperation must have got through, someone was smiling down at me and we made it for the funeral. I think my mother gave me one of the biggest hugs ever when I arrived! I still miss my grandmother but, as the eldest granddaughter, was given her pearls which I treasure and will pass to Laura on my death. Also, I have had the joy of knowing a remarkable woman who brought happiness into many people's lives.

So it was a really hard start to the year. Then I found myself unbelievably pregnant. I couldn't believe it, after all that waiting, I was to have another baby. My sister-in-law was pregnant again too and we would have our babies within 2 or 3 weeks of each other. Somehow though, I never really felt pregnant and I constantly tested myself to see if it was true by doing things like shifting our bed to vacuum under it. I noticed everyone else was much more excited about it than I was, I had to pretend. At the same time it seemed right: my grandmother had died and I was to have another baby.

Sadly it was not to be. I went to Sainsbury's one day and carried some heavy shopping back. I met a GP from the practice where I worked who duly berated me. We were going to have a Chinese meal that evening and Iain went out to get it but we never ate the meal. While he was out I started to bleed. Later on that evening it was clear that I was miscarrying and I was admitted to hospital, into the maternity unit. I remember the GP visiting and noticed that she had written in the notes *appears to be coping well*. I couldn't believe that she had said that; no one, not even I, knew the well of pain I felt at that time. It was only later that I dared face up to it.

Although I had privacy and was given excellent care in the hospital, there was something quite surreal about it hearing babies crying some distance away. I was taken to theatre the next day and discharged later.

I was given no emotional support. In fact I was left; abandoned was the only way I could describe it but then I didn't want to see anyone. They didn't know how to deal with me and I didn't want to talk. The only visitor was the vicar and I was quite definitely angry with God at the time, so I'm not sure he got much of a reception but at least he came! I do remember outside the school gate someone I knew, not a close friend, just touched me on the shoulder and asked me how I was and actually meaning it. That touch meant so much. Most people don't know how to deal with someone else's grief, and unless you have had a miscarriage, you don't know what it's like, to lose an unknown, unsexed, unnamed baby but who was your baby nevertheless. We have, what I perceive to be a particularly unhelpful custom in this country, not to tell people we're pregnant until we're 12 weeks just in case. That is denying celebrating something and denying the opportunity to grieve if sadly it is taken away. If nobody knows you are pregnant then there's nobody to share this deep sadness with; a sadness that remains and is very much a part of me to this day.

I was angry, I blamed God: how could he have made me pregnant after all this time, if only to take it away from me? I know that defies logic but that was how I felt. I buried the grief even to the point of being *fine* on the baby's due date and *fine* when my sister-in-law's baby was born and now he is the only poignant reminder of what might have been.

So that was it really; but maybe it wasn't. Because I had got pregnant, the hope had returned that maybe I would conceive again but of course the biological clock was ticking fast; I was 37 years old. No more pregnancies. Only in my dreams and I have had so many of those and sometimes still do. I dream I am pregnant but there is no bump, it isn't real.

My response was to lose myself in my work as the next chapter describes.

More about Secondary Infertility

Little is written about *secondary infertility*. However, I did discover one book [1] in which this condition is described as being kept 'in the closet' and not talked about much. It could be because those couples experiencing it can feel as if they are caught between two worlds, *belonging* neither to the world of the childless nor to the world of the fertile. It can be a lonely place. Indeed it has been a joy to read this book which recounts the experiences of other women who have been given a diagnosis of secondary infertility. In it I see these women's experiences which very much resemble my own.

The book describes the emotional impact which includes the feeling of self-blame. Was I to blame for this inability to conceive? Was it because I smoked? What was wrong with me and my body? There were feelings of inadequacy and failure. I was only half a woman. These feelings build on what may already exist about feeling 'not good enough'. Then there's the guilt of feeling that you should consider yourself lucky because you do have one child but are living with that longing for another. Associated with the sadness that you are going through is the lack of enjoyment of the child you do have.

There is also the anger aimed at women who seem to fall pregnant so easily and jealousy towards those close to you who become pregnant. As I have already said, at the time I was going through investigations and treatment, my sister-in-law and my best friend were both pregnant with their second children. Every time I saw them, all I saw were their pregnancies becoming more and more obvious. I didn't want to see them; I didn't want to speak to them. How could they not see my pain? These feelings were less acute but still there, as I listened to friends bemoaning the impact of their children on their lives, longing for them to go to school and hating the way their children constantly fought.

I have also read other women's accounts of their experiences of secondary infertility. It was the headlines that struck me: *Secondary infertility hurts differently, but just as much* written by a lady called Melissa. So much of her experiences mirror my own. What other people unthinkingly say about family sizes reminds me of the statistics of the time for the 'normal' family of 2.2 children. Have you noticed, for example, how family packs in the supermarket are always in 4's or multiples of 4. Some of what Melissa says I hadn't considered but reading her words they are so true. Having had one child "*I know what I'm missing*".

A lot of this is about loss. It's about the loss of the family which had been longed for but never born and then the loss of the mother role; only having had one chance, no sibling rivalry. It's something I have experienced having had two siblings in my family of origin, but will never experience as a mother and something that Iain has never experienced at all.

Miscarriage

And then miscarriage: there does seem to be a little research into the emotional impact but there is nothing surprising about it. It's grief again. What struck me most was an article from the BBC news website entitled *Doctors unaware of miscarriage grief*. It called for doctors not to disregard miscarriage as a minor matter. This article was published in 2000, so it was even sadder to see an article entitled *Miscarriage: must doctors make our grief worse?* published in the Times in 2007. A woman will already have developed a bond with this unborn child and may have fantasised about what the baby will look like, what family life will become and maybe the relationship with other siblings if there are any. There's also the loss of dreams [2]. Before having a baby most parents will have a fantasy about that child. With miscarriage that dream is dashed, as is also the vision or dream of what the completed family will be like and both partners will experience grief in their own way. Iain feels passionately about miscarriage and he often wonders whether the redundancy he experienced a few years after our loss was because he had supported a member of his team returning home to be with his wife who was miscarrying. This appeared to go against the ethos of the company. Men may also experience *a complex set of thoughts, feelings and considerable confusion about appropriate behaviour* [3]. They are expected to support the woman but in truth they are experiencing a grief process of their own.

It took me a very long time to acknowledge and appreciate the enormity of the grief and loss associated with these experiences and to know that what I was feeling was normal and not to feel that I should just get over it. Many women will experience the same or similar emotions but for different reasons. For example, divorce and loss of a once loved partner or a marriage, or illness such as breast cancer and loss of health and body image. Grief is a normal process which we all go through at a time of loss but I believe for some of the losses I have described in this book we have a tendency to suppress those feelings, partly because we fear that they will overwhelm us and also because we have a tendency to minimize them. When do you finally say you have lost that chance to have another child? After the miscarriage I went on hoping month after month that I would become pregnant again. It is difficult to grieve about something that can only achieve closure, in this case at menopause.

Grief and Loss

Grief is an overwhelmingly painful emotion but is a completely normal response to loss of any sort. I am going to briefly describe Kubler-Ross's well known stages of grief which is recognized by others [4] as being experienced by many of us when we go through any significant life change:

Denial: We don't want to believe the event is going to happen or has happened so we deny it.

Anger: Then you become angry. If you have lost someone you love you may be angry with a doctor, a nurse, anyone. As I have already said, at the time of the miscarriage I was angry with God, my friend, my sister-in-law to name but a few.

Bargaining: We try to make deals to get back what we've lost; we ask for something while promising another.

Depression: I don't think I need to explain what I mean by that, most of us know. I now see that the depression I experienced was a response to grief but was unaware of it at the time because I minimized what I had been through.

Acceptance: At some point we decide to be at peace with the way things are. Nothing is going to change or to bring back that or who we have lost. I will be writing about my process of acceptance in chapter 8.

However, I have come to see that our loss becomes part of who we are and we can even see it as a gift. If we look there will be nuggets there, something that can, in fact, enrich our lives and help us make sense of something that may have seemed so senseless and unfair. In the later chapters of this book I hope that you will see how I have used those nuggets to help me find a strong purpose in my life.

Feelings and Emotions

Grief is an emotion and a very painful emotion and I want to share with you now some of what I've learnt about emotions and feelings over the past few years. I want to help you develop your own understanding of your feelings and to welcome them rather than be afraid. I think my story alone gives justification for starting to understand our own feelings and emotions. I have also read some very powerful descriptions from other women who have faced incredibly difficult periods in their life who, having confronted those feelings, have moved on to do amazing things. Many of you will have read *Eat, Pray, Love* [5] or seen the film. The author describes how she found herself on the bathroom floor night after night sobbing as she faced her feelings of shame, guilt, confusion and fear arising out of the unhappiness of her marriage. The book continues with her journey out of this pain to find peace again. In the next chapter I will refer to Brene Brown [6] whose life's work has been researching shame and the importance of facing up to that but in doing so found herself face to face with her own pain.

Emotions are part of the normal functioning human being. They make a huge contribution to our fully experiencing our lives. We suffer emotional pain for the same reason as we suffer physical pain. The reason for experiencing this pain is that our body and our brain are trying to get our attention and we must therefore attend to it. I have read various descriptions that normalise emotions as being part of the human experience. For example, we tend to see and shy away from people who are experiencing strong emotions as though there is something wrong. Learning to be with our emotions and feelings enables us to be more rounded human beings and to more fully experience our lives [8]. Of course, there are very positive emotions as well as the painful ones. Let's learn to appreciate them all! We need to recognise them for what they are: something which can change and go away. We are not our feelings!

Key Points of Chapter 4

- Grief and loss are normal responses to many life events and it is important to acknowledge those feelings
- Secondary infertility has its own unique set of responses and associated feelings
- Not enough attention is given to the emotional impact of miscarriage
- Learning to fully experience and to be with our emotions gives us a greater and more enriching experience of life

Moments to Ponder

Start to fully experience your emotional life and remember there are times when you feel on top of the world, as well as the more painful emotions. I want you to learn to fully experience them all. I am going to ask you to notice when you are feeling something and to describe that feeling. This is variously described as process coaching [8] or focusing [7]. It may sound a bit way-out at first but believe me it's worth a try:

Where are you feeling this in your body? ....
....
....
....
....

Fully focus your attention on and describe it: size, texture, colour. Does it make a noise? if it smelt or tasted of something, what would it be?

....
....
....
....

Keep focusing on it and see if it changes in any way, then go through the process again. Keep doing this and eventually the feeling will go away. Notice how they change and go away. Refer back to your feel-good list if you are faced with a feeling low time. You can make a conscious choice to feel better.

Notes ....
....
....
....
....
....
....
....
....
....
....

Activity log

What is my learning from reading this chapter and working through
the exercise? ....
....
....
....

What actions am I going to take as a result? ....
....
....
....

By when am I going to have done it/them? ....
....
....
....

What is the benefit of accomplishing this action? ....
....
....
....

What is the cost of not accomplishing this action? ....
....
....
....
....

Chapter 5

An emotional rollercoaster

I often wonder how many other women there are out there who, like me, can honestly and truthfully describe the experience of motherhood as being something amazing and something wonderful. I also wonder how many other women struggle in silence, like me, with the undoubted difficulties of this incredibly hard job for which we have no training. At the same time, not for one minute could I ever regret the decision to have a baby. It has given me the greatest fulfilment of my life. I feel this most intensely right now as I revise this chapter in the train going through France into Germany to meet my baby grandson for the first time. I am reminded of hearing someone say once that one of the most fulfilling times of her life was nursing her dying mother. In other words fulfilment is not always filled with great excitement or happiness, it is about something else deeper than that. Motherhood is indeed a paradox [1] as already discussed in Chapter 3.

I have called this chapter *An Emotional Rollercoaster* because I want to dispel the whole 'yummy mummy' myth created by the media which views the experience of motherhood, I believe, through rose-tinted spectacles. For me, those years of full-on motherhood (0-18, or so years) were beset with a range of emotions, not to mention the grief that I have already described There were times when being a mum was indeed a joyful and fulfilling experience and there is no doubt that having a child is the ultimate experience of being a woman. After all, that is at the basis of our biology. But there is also the guilt experienced by so many women and that is what I want to focus on in this chapter. I think it is this, more than anything else, that tainted my experience of motherhood. I have since realised that it doesn't have to be like this. We have choice and we can choose to let that burden of guilt go. It is my intention that the exercises at the end of this chapter will help you begin to do just that.

A Mother's Guilt

After I lost the baby, I buried the grief and made some kind of adjustment to being the mother of one or to use that awful expression an 'only child' with all the judgments that are implicit in those words. At some point I came across the French (*fille unique*) and the Italian (*figlia unica*) terms which made me feel that my daughter was something really special. I have read about the unfair stigma that is attached to the 'only child' from an author who prefers to use the term *single child,* as I intend to do from now on [2]. Single children are often judged to be 'spoilt' and the parents of single children are accused of being selfish; a judgment based solely on a false assumption that a choice has been made to have just one child. I have always told people that this was not mine or Iain's choice. Being the mother of a single child and the wife of another, I can only see it as being very hard for the child. If you look at your love, your attention and your aspirations as a spotlight you shine on your children then look how bright and strong and direct that light is on a single child and how much wider that beam is on two, three or more children. Yes, one child can enjoy the material things that may not be possible when there are more children but there is an intensity in that light beam that may be hard for that child to bear at times.

It was important for me to return to work after maternity leave, in the main because of my mental health but it also made so much difference to Laura. She had been a baby who would scream when faced with too many adults. After starting with the childminder she changed to the hugely sociable person she is today. I can't remember the name of the childminder but I will be eternally grateful to her for the love and care she gave to Laura which allowed me to go back to work. But of course going back to work is not as easy as it sounds. Any woman reading this will remember that first day back at work and the guilt she felt in leaving her baby. I well remember that day even now. I was working as a health visitor in Harlow in Essex and in the lunch hour I went into the town centre and bought her a little pair of cotton dungarees with a teddy bear pattern to in some way assuage that guilt!

Guilt is like a heavy weight that we carry but what is it and where does it come from? Parents have blogged aplenty on the subject with some great quotes: "*Maternal guilt – it comes with the placenta*", "*How perfect do we expect to be?*", "*We need to lower the bar*". In an article written by Lorraine Candy in the Mail Online, the first pangs arrive as soon as you know that you're pregnant and remember the glass of wine you drank or the mayonnaise on your salad the night before!

According to a recent poll, 74% of working mothers say they feel guilty about leaving their children. There has been plenty of research over the years expressing concerns about children of working mothers, so it was refreshing to read a study carried out by the University of Texas in 2005 which concluded that although there may be a few negative impacts in the early years, they had all disappeared by the time children were 10 years of age.

So where does all this guilt start? Is it in the past because of the fantasies we have about parenthood? I know I created some very high standards about how I would be as a mother. Also, I only had one child and all my hopes were focused on that one child and not just my hopes and aspirations. I only had one chance to get it 'right' whatever that means. I think it probably started for me in those early days when I was unable to settle my screaming baby. Although in my head I understood why that might be: she could smell the milk, she could feel my stress; I judged myself harshly that I just wasn't good enough.

I have already described what happened when I started giving Laura solids and, apart from the irrational anger I felt, my failure to give her home-cooked foods further compounded my feelings of guilt. I judged myself as having failed yet again and the food thing was to become such a big issue. Coming from a home of post-war rationing and shortages, food was never wasted; we ate what was put in front of us. I ended up using the dreaded tins of baby food but at least that way she would eat and meal times were calmer. However, she couldn't do that for ever. Her diet became so limited because I just couldn't get her to eat healthily and there was me, the health visitor, promoting good nutrition and completely failing with my own child. I remember the embarrassment I felt meeting clients in the supermarket with my ill-concealed box of *Frosties* in my trolley. Meal times became a battle ground sometimes between myself and Iain too. No wonder food held no joy for her.

I hated to see her upset and I couldn't allow Iain to be hard on her. No consistency, my fault, I gave in all the time, I couldn't say *No*. I was so afraid she would reject me. I set up a vicious circle for myself and I see it now. I was so afraid I would lose her love and that would be the final proof of what a bad mother I was. It was all reinforced by the criticism I perceived coming from those around me. I created a very lonely world for myself where I wouldn't let anyone in to help me with the incredibly hard job of being a mum.

Were any of these judgments true? I don't think so. Part of the personal work I have done over the last few years is accepting that I did the best I could but even in the darkest days I never stopped loving her and that unconditional love, I believe, is the greatest gift we offer our children. The importance of love has since been researched and proved by advances in neuroscience [3].

The really sad thing for me now, looking back, is the time she needed me most after the suicide of a friend and I wasn't available for her because of my own mental ill health. Her behaviour at the time was telling me but all I was able to see was this adolescent/young woman doing everything in her power to upset me. She would stay out late. I would stay up worrying and waiting, going to work in the morning exhausted. I bitterly regret that I didn't have the insight I have now. My attempts at being superwoman and living on the hamster wheel made me ill. But regret is not the same as guilt and after many years I am able to forgive myself. Our relationship was built on strong enough foundations that it has survived.

What is Guilt?

My own experience and that of so many women I have worked with over the years, first as a health visitor and then as a coach, has made me become increasingly curious about this whole concept of *guilt*. It becomes an incredible burden which no one asks us to carry except ourselves. Of all the emotions I have experienced, it seems the most difficult to understand, to manage and to shake off. I started my research by trying to find a definition. The definitions describe people being tried and found guilty of something. So I wonder is that what we do? Try ourselves and find ourselves guilty? Of what? I can only conclude that in my case and I am sure it is the same for many other women we judge ourselves as not being a perfect mother. In fact, what we need to be is good enough, as Donald Winnicott reminds us:

> "*The good enough mother ... starts off with an almost complete adaptation to her infant's needs, and as time proceeds she adapts less and less completely, gradually, according to the infant's growing ability to deal with her failure*" [4].

In contrast, the perfect mother satisfies all the needs of the infant on the spot and this can prevent him from developing. By failing to do that we are giving our children more realistic expectations of the world. Another definition is provided by Wikipedia:

> "*a cognitive or an emotional experience that occurs when a person realizes or believes accurately or not – that they have violated a moral standard, and bear sole responsibility for that violation*".

Makes sense? I think so. Somehow as mothers many of us feel we have total responsibility to bring up our children, care for our homes, our partners and hold down often a full-time job and in addition to that we may be trying to rise to the top of the career ladder. And guess what? Somewhere along the line we are probably unable to reach our high standards and we judge ourselves as not good enough. The result is guilt. Why do we do it to ourselves?

Hypothesising about a Mother's Guilt

In this section I want to share a couple of reasons why I believe we share this phenomenon of guilt. I firstly want to look at the impact of the feminist movement and remind ourselves that men and women are different. Then I'd like to introduce you to the amazing work of Brene Brown [5], an American researcher. I believe that the key may lie in her work.

Everyone reading this book will have grown up in an era in which there have been great advances for women giving them greater freedom. We have far greater choice but I have seen that choice described as a double-edged sword [6]: we can choose to have babies or not, improvements in contraception have seen to that. It is less than a hundred years since women were given the vote. It was during the First World War that an increasing number of women came out of service and into jobs traditionally filled by men. Domestic violence against women is now universally condemned and legislated against. Women who have babies outside of marriage are no longer ostracised.

When I was first a mother, there were less of us going out to work than is the case now and there has been a growth in our materialistic society that has given women the feeling that they have little choice but to work. Having said that, I do now see an increasing number of women turning their backs on the corporate world to give themselves the greater flexibility of self-employment. A new word has crept into our vocabulary: the *mumpreneur*. There is also an increasing pressure on parents to ensure their children achieve.

There have been many advances for pregnant women and mothers over the past few years in terms of improved maternity pay, leave and legislation to prevent discrimination in the workplace but with that comes enormous expectations and pressure placed upon women to successfully juggle careers and motherhood. In some high level jobs, the expectation seems to be that the woman is back at work hormone free, fully functioning and returning swiftly to their pre-pregnancy size and shape within a very short time. I was shocked to read that a French minister was back working within what seems like hours of giving birth. The media were celebrating this as a major achievement. Not only that, mothers are meant to love it and bring up high achieving children with enormous IQ's. It's too much!

This was endorsed by Professor John Cox in a 2004 article in the Guardian written by Anna Moore. His argument was that the lack of support available to mothers and the unrealistic expectations we have in our culture for mothers to be contributing to society is linked to the higher incidence of postnatal depression in this country, guilt being one of the symptoms. In other countries, Japan for example, it is traditional for women to spend the first month after delivery with their parents who care for both mother and baby. It is also worth remembering that in this country it is only 50 years or so ago that middle class women had a lying in period of a month.

Men and Women are Different

The truth so often ignored in our egalitarian society is that men and women are actually programmed in a very different way. We have evolved from a time when men and women had very defined roles. Men were hunter-gatherers and women kept the home and looked after the children. *Things were simple. He was the lunch chaser, she was the nest defender* [7, p13]. We now have evidence which concludes that men and women have evolved differently both mentally and physically [7]. Hooray! Let's celebrate it!

Our parents, grandparents and generations before had similar simplicity of roles. Now things are far more confusing. Neither sex is certain of their roles. Men and women are different and when we strive for equality we have to be clear about what we are asking for. Equality is not the same as being identical.

I feel that the feminist movement, which was so instrumental in stopping the exploitation of women and in giving us the opportunities we have today, has gone too far. It does not acknowledge these essential differences. Instead, it puts pressure on us to be this super person capable of doing everything and doing it to a high standard. And guess what? We fail! I was glad when I read Susie Heath's view that feminism had gone too far and killed the spirit of femininity [8]. It reinforced my own opinion and supported the belief that if we step into our feminine energy and power, we can make a real difference in the world by creating balance and what I wonder, has all this got to do with guilt? I think it means we can stop being who we think we should be and start to reclaim who we truly are, including reclaiming our femininity. I will be returning to this theme again in the next chapter, because I also believe that much of the stress we experience is because we are not being our true, authentic selves.

Developing Forgiveness and Self Compassion

So what can we do to start unburdening ourselves from guilt and why is it important that we do it?

We need to learn self-compassion and we need to let go of being perfect. We need to accept our imperfections and just feel that we are enough. This is what Brene Brown [5] urges us to do. Easier said than done I know! She argues that what we do is strive to be perfect at all things because we are trying to earn approval and acceptance from those around us and we don't want anyone to see our shame which in her terms is a sense of being bad. We feel guilty because of our 'badness' which in fact is our imperfection and our normal human frailty. None of this in any way prevents us from striving to be the best we can but in a healthy way and learning self-compassion enables us to let go of the guilt which can weigh so heavily on us.

Brown introduces the concept of self-compassion and includes this quote by Christopher K Germer and what a lovely quote this is:

"A moment of self-compassion can change your entire day, A string of such moments can change the course of your life". [5, p59]

To be self-compassionate we need to be kind to ourselves and to be warm and understanding of our inadequacies rather than ignoring the pain we feel or judging ourselves.

I now want to introduce another author with other ideas, ideas which can help us as we try to change the way we think and feel about ourselves and our world. I have found her work to be inspirational on my journey. She is Barbara Frederickson who has written a book called *Positivity* [9]. Her scientific research conclusively proves that positive emotions can:

> "*Open our hearts and minds, making us more receptive and more creative*" [p21]

> "*Allow us to discover and build new skills, new ties, new knowledge, and new ways of being.*" [p24]

In other words, adopting positivity can be transformational.

But let's not forget that there are some negative emotions that are essential to our very survival. For example, without fear we would not be able to act when our life or our safety is threatened. However, there are other negative emotions that Frederickson describes as gratuitous. They do not serve us nor do they serve those closest to us. We can make a conscious choice to change our emotions. It's not easy, our brains need reprogramming to adopt a more positive outlook and it can be done even if we have to start by faking it! In making that choice we can improve our experience of life and indeed our physical health. She lists ten forms of positivity:

Joy
Gratitude
Serenity
Interest
Hope
Pride
Amusement
Inspiration
Awe
Love

I have no room here to go into this in any depth and I urge anyone who is interested in this idea of positivity to read the book. What we do know is that those who have a more optimistic outlook can live an extra 8 years of good quality life [10] and what we need to do is experience 3 or more of these positive emotions to every one negative emotion to have a more fulfilling life [9].

Isn't that what we want and wouldn't that help us neutralise the guilt? I strongly believe it works.

key Points of Chapter 5

- The experience of motherhood can be an emotional rollercoaster
- The emotion of guilt is experienced by many women and is a heavy burden
- It may be due to the expectations of women and our strive for perfection
- Choosing positive emotions is a way of unburdening ourselves as is adopting self-compassion and the sense that what we are enough

Moments to Ponder

By doing these exercises I want you to feel more positive and more forgiving of yourself.

I want you to make the conscious choice to turn the negative emotion of guilt into the positive emotion of gratitude. It is quite simple and can be done by adopting a practice of gratitude. My request to you is that every day you list 3 things to be grateful for. These can range from something big to something you might normally take for granted. Even on the darkest days there will be something. Look for the little things like your child's smile, the sun shining, birds in the garden or food on your table. Some people write down their gratitudes, some people say them like prayers. I tend to write mine down as I write my journal. It's not a ritual but it does focus my thoughts as I reflect on my day. You will find what works for you and as you maintain this practice you will notice how much more positive you feel.

The other thing that I know works because I've done it, is affirmation. So create some for yourself and repeat them on a daily basis in front of a mirror. One way to do this is to write down all the negative beliefs you have about yourself and turn them into positives. For example, *I will never earn enough money to give me the life-style I want* becomes *My income gives me the abundant lifestyle I deserve*. Or, *I will never be able to have the career I really want* becomes *I have a rich and exciting career*. The same can be done for the way we look. We can turn around *I'm fat and ugly* to *I am gorgeous*. Note that every affirmation must be in the present. It is also important to be consistent about this for at least 30 days; you can and you will re-programme your mind [11]. Research shows us that this works, otherwise why would so many people do it?

Develop self-compassion, warmth and understanding for being less than perfect. Tell yourself that you are enough.

Well maybe that's enough for now. I hope that by doing this work you are beginning to feel lighter in your mind and if you can only do one of these exercises make that the gratitude one. I know so many people who have found and find that so helpful.

Activity log

What is my learning from reading this chapter and working through the exercise? ....
....
....
....
....

What actions am I going to take as a result? ....
....
....
....
....

By when am I going to have done it/them? ....
....
....
....
....

What is the benefit of accomplishing this action? ....
....
....
....
....

What is the cost of not accomplishing this action? ....
....
....
....
....

Notes ....
....
....
....
....
....
....
....

Chapter 6

The hamster wheel

There are so many women I know who can identify with this idea of a hamster wheel, which we get on and can't seem to get off. It doesn't make us happy, it doesn't keep us well and we get no pleasure or enjoyment from being on it unless it is the adrenaline fix that we get on a daily basis. It is my time on the hamster wheel that forms the focus of this chapter. I want to tell you why I may have behaved like this and I also want to remind us all that we do have a choice. So many of us feel stuck on that wheel, feeling we have no choice, and that is just how life is. I now feel quite evangelistic about it all and to use a cliché, life is not a dress rehearsal.

One of the many things I have learnt over the last few years is that we all have far more choice than we think we have. I have also learnt that there is only one person that can make things different in our lives and that is ourselves, and we really do need to take greater responsibility for the way we live our lives. However, we also have to recognise that we can't always do it alone and for me it has made a powerful difference working with a coach. There will be more about that in later chapters. I am also going to tell you about the five ways of wellbeing in this chapter, because if you are on this hamster wheel and you recognise your behaviour from my story, one of the first things you will need to do is to start to look after yourself better. Adopting the five ways of wellbeing is a way of making a real difference to your daily life right now. And they're not a big deal!

Moving On
As I saw it, after everything that had happened, I now had to move

on with my life. All the anger and grief, I had to put them behind me and get on. What's more, I felt I had to manage this myself and after all I was a competent person, of course I could cope. So I pushed it all down into a metaphorical bin and moved on. There was too much pain to deal with. Even now I look back and there is still a tendency to minimise the enormity of what happened. Yet I know if I start to think too deeply the tears will come, the sadness is still there and it always will be. I minimised the enormity of both losses associated with the secondary infertility and the miscarriage, which were compounded by the death of my grandmother. This is a kind of grief that goes unacknowledged, is not understood and is rarely spoken about. No one knows how you feel because you don't talk about it.

At the time of the miscarriage I was working as a practice nurse and I had started studying for my degree. So I jumped wholeheartedly into my career. I successfully applied to go onto the health visiting bank and took whatever work came my way. At home, I tried to be the best mother and wife that I could be by providing the best home for my family. That way, no one could judge me as failing even though I judged myself as a failure in what was the most important thing to me: being a mother and raising a family or the 'normal' family of 2.2 children. I always felt that there was something not normal about only having one child. You are always asked, *How old are your children?* Then comes the explanation. I did not want to be judged as selfish because I only had one child. I felt fiercely protective of Laura and didn't want her to experience the prejudice that is meted out to the spoilt 'only child'. I remember going to the headmaster at the primary school after hearing this judgment made about Laura by a supply teacher. How many times have I wanted to scream *I didn't choose to only have one child?*

Indeed one of the reasons cited for parents choosing to have more than one child is that they do fear that a single child may be 'spoilt' or may 'suffer' [1]. I have to admit that there were very definite material advantages for us all in terms of Laura's activities. She would not have had the opportunities for riding and riding holidays, ballet, music and all the other things she did if we had had more children. Many would argue that children need the company of siblings but she always had lots of friends, particularly in her early years and formed close bonds with her cousins. However, I would always notice with her that after a period of time with other children she always needed to go off on her own for a while, one time even leaving her own birthday party for a bit of peace and quiet!

Getting on the Hamster Wheel

So I created this hamster wheel which I spun round in for the next 14 years. After working on the health visiting bank for a few years, I successfully applied for a part-time health visiting post and left my practice nursing role. I'm surprised that I didn't try and juggle the two! I wholeheartedly threw myself into the job with far greater zeal and passion than I had previously.

Very early on in those years, some research took place in Cambridge, the area where I lived and worked, which found that health visitors had very successful results when providing listening visits to mothers assessed as having post-natal depression. That work continues to grow and there is absolutely no doubt as to its importance, because research is showing us the impact on babies, children and young people of having a postnatally depressed mother [2, 3, 4]. As I now return to working in this field, the evidence is growing which shows that specially trained health visitors can be effective in not only making a positive intervention with women identified as having postnatal depression [5] but that they may also prevent its onset [6]. As far as I am concerned, it beggars belief that this is not a part of every health visitor's work and that they are not properly trained and resourced to enable this care to take place. Any financial excuses do not stand up when you look at the costs to the country of caring for the mother in or out of hospital, the impact on the child which may be long lasting and the long-term impact on the woman and her family.

For me all those years ago, that time was a moment of epiphany: *This is what health visitors were put on the earth to do*. However, I still had no insight into my own mental health and what had happened to me when Laura was born. That remained buried in that metaphorical bin under everything else I was throwing on top of it.

I was a passionate advocate of this work. I well remember the first time I visited a lady and asked her to complete the Edinburgh Postnatal Depression Scale (EPDS). This was a scale developed in the 1980's and has since been widely used to help identify women who have postnatal depression but it has had a checkered history, in part because health visitors have not been adequately trained in its use. But we were. This lady scored highly on question 10 which asks the woman to say if she ever has thoughts of harming herself. This was a lady who, when I had visited her in the past, said very little and the visits were soon over. Now that I was able to help her, I discovered that she was seriously self-harming and that she was clinically depressed and I was able to refer her for appropriate services for herself and her children. I found that this work helped women talk about their experiences of being abused as children, of domestic violence and a wealth of other things. Making a difference to these women's lives became of enormous importance in my life as did health visiting. What I didn't realise was the impact it was having on me.

I always seemed to be wanting more. Any opportunities that came along, I was up for it. I was passionate about what I did, I was hungry and I wanted to influence practice. Looking back, I probably wanted to do anything except think about the miscarriage, the loss of any subsequent children and my grandmother's death and grieve. I increased my hours by taking any bank work going and of course the money was good too but I still wanted more. Health visiting alone was never enough. So I greedily grabbed opportunities as they came along. I joined the practice development group and applied for the role of primary care team leader. Eventually I acted as professional lead for health visiting and then successfully applied for the job but I was always fighting for something. First it was having the job graded higher. I won that one. I also got funding for various courses for the health visitors and school nurses and I got myself a desk at the Primary Care Group (PCG) offices. I even moved my practice area, something I will always regret, to try and make the job more manageable. But when it came to having the hours reviewed, that was my big failure. The job was half time clinical practice and half time professional lead and was always a juggle. I remember one real dilemma: I had a child protection report and a paper for the PCG board to write, same deadline and no give. I have no idea what the outcome was but I remember not knowing where to turn or what to do.

While this was going on, I filled in for 6 months as nurse member of the PCG board which I loved. I loved it all but looking back I have no idea how I thought I could do it all. In addition, I even started studying for a m aster's degree. I think most people thought I was mad but it felt important and so it proved; it was utterly transformational.

All the time Laura was growing up. We had some lovely times together. Shopping was one of our greatest pleasures and again I found it hard to say no. I started to rack up the credit cards, not seriously, but I think it was literally retail therapy. When she was younger we used to go up to London on a day out; sometimes seeing the sights, sometimes going to the theatre and always a visit to Hamleys toy shop. I remember well the IRA bomb scares and on one occasion being evacuated from Oxford Circus station moving as fast as possible up the escalator whilst trying to remain calm for Laura's sake.

As she grew into her teenage tears, we were close initially but then drew apart. I feel sad looking back that when she really needed me I was emotionally unable to be there for her but thankfully things have changed in many ways for both of us now!

Why Choose the Hamster Wheel Experience?

What is it like on that hamster wheel? There's a feeling of no choice but to be on that wheel. We become victims of the circumstances we find ourselves in. Somewhere deep inside we are not hearing our spirit crying out to be heard. I know that I am not alone in this type of behaviour. Part of me was doing this so I didn't have to address or feel that pain of losing my baby and with that, probably the last chance to have a second child but at the same time I was trying to prove something to myself.

There are several things going on here that I want to reflect on and there is a major consequence. There's a tendency for some of us to believe that we are the great copers of the world and that we can do it all but the time will come when that metaphorical bin lid flies open and the contents, all our unacknowledged thoughts and feelings, fall out all over the place. Stress can affect us both physically and mentally and we are all affected in different ways. I will come to that later on. In the meantime, let us ask why we do it? What we don't realise when we're in this situation is that we do have a choice, although somehow we don't see it when we're stuck in this pattern of behaviour. As women, what we also deny or not allow ourselves is to be vulnerable. Are we afraid of acknowledging it? Do we see it as a weakness?

Women have got themselves into all kinds of a mess by trying to have it all and do it all. In my mother's day it took all of her time to rear a family and run a house and maybe have a part-time job as my mother did. I'm not arguing for a return to that as I know that working has given me so much and I always enjoyed it up until the end. Funny that it feels as though the work I have done since becoming self-employed is not work! I see the end was when I left health visiting, not the years since.

I wanted to say yes to everything, because it all seemed so important but I actually think I always said yes because I was never satisfied with what I had nor was I any good at saying no! I remember my boss saying once to me that I was capable of so much more than this job demanded. There were times when I blamed her for what happened but maybe her comment was far more insightful than I felt at the time. I do believe that the NHS held me back and I remember saying to myself *It's stifled my creativity*. When I left, there was enormous relief at being able to work with my ideas and to be able to deliver high quality work because I had the time. What's more, I was paid decent money for it.

At home things were the same. I had to be the best mum, the best wife, the best at her career, the best housewife and the best jam maker. I can hardly believe I was so committed to making jam! It was cakes at weekends and a roast dinner on Sundays because that is what I thought every good working wife and mum ought to do. I even tried getting a cleaner, twice, but that didn't work out because I was paying someone to do something that I couldn't really trust them to do properly! I look back now and think about Laura rejecting the more conventional life-style of university, which of course I thought she should follow and instead, working on the local American USAF base doing waitressing. I also well remember a friend saying to me that it looked as though Laura felt she could never aspire to my high standards, so maybe she was making a choice to opt out. It took a while for the real meaning of that statement to sink in but when it did I was shocked. Here was a big learning experience for me.

I have recently read a paper of a local colleague [7] and have used his research to underpin my own thoughts which has resulted in me proposing the following features of stress in women:

Emotional attachment: women who experience stress appear to measure their value by their impact on others. Making others in their lives happy, their children, their employers, their parents and whoever else is in their lives.

Unwanted demand: women who experience stress will often complain about the amount expected of them, again by their families and their employers.

Unrealistic expectations: Jane Kenyon has coined the term *Strong Woman Syndrome* (www.wellheeleddivas.co.uk) which she sees as the behaviour of women who have incredibly high expectations of themselves. The aim of these women and there are many of them, is to be perfect in every role they take on. To do that they need to be in control of everything.

Feeling unsupported: The consequence is they feel unsupported and undervalued by everyone and are reluctant to ask for help.

Do you recognise any of this? Because I know that that was me and that's why, when I first read it, it struck such a chord!

Because we take on so much, the only way we can manage it is to be in complete control. I remember it even mattered to me that the socks were lined up in pairs on the washing line! That was one way of me controlling a really challenging world and it became unsustainable as the next chapter will show. We also resist asking for help because in our efforts to be in complete control of this crazy world we are creating, we think we do everything better than everyone else.

Embracing Our Femininity

As I see it, the three big issues are stress, choice and being women. Regarding the final point, as I said in the last chapter, I really believe that in all the striving for equality we have lost our way of what we're really about. I have already referred to Susie Heath [8], whose argument is that in our complaint that men have too long ruled the world that we have collaborated with them and have tried to become pseudo-men. This isn't working for us. I remember when I was doing my masters degree, coming across the beginning of this argument which has grown over the years. I find it really exciting because it takes us back to our origins; in Susie's words, our *"authentic feminine."* The book I picked up then related to nursing [9] and I see the author, Jean Watson's argument as a microcosm of the larger world. What she suggests is that nurses go into the profession to heal and to care but find themselves being defeated by what she terms *institutional oppression.* She asks a question *"For its souls's sake, will nursing own its own science phenomena and stop duplicating medicine at every turn? Or is nursing still, after all, just a subset of medicine, choosing to remain inside its tent, complaining all the while, and withering away its gifts of life and living and healing?"* [p xxiv]. Both Susie and Jean remind us of the need for balance between the yin and the yang, female and male energy. They mutually help each other and together provide equilibrium and harmony. In the smaller world of health, the balance is between the healing and curing processes.

Susie describes how both these energies have a dependent, interdependent and co-dependent relationship. The world needs both the strong, productive and focused male energy and the creative, gentle and nurturing female energy to thrive. My own vision is for women to step into their female energy and to lead from that place and in that way we can create a more harmonious world. Men will be happier, less competitive as they will no longer have to live from the extreme of their male energy. Women will be happier too as they allow their partner to help them and they allow themselves to be vulnerable. I know that as I have accepted my vulnerability that I am a more rounded person. That in no way prevents me from having a fulfilling career and myself and my husband having an equal relationship. In no way do I suggest that women should be repressed but be honoured and honour themselves for who they are. In the same way, I believe nurses should be valued for who they are and complementary, rather than subservient, to their medical colleagues. In standing firm and confident in their female energy, women will be able to move off their hamster wheel, which is both unhealthy and unhelpful to them and their relationships.

Opting to do nothing about this will cause us as individuals undoubted stress. It also serves to reduce our confidence and self-esteem as we are not being true to ourselves but it does nothing to improve the world either. With more of the feminine energy in the world, I strongly believe that the world will be a better place: less poverty, less violence, greater optimism and a better chance of putting an end to the major threats we face in the 21st Century: climate change, terrorism and financial meltdown.

Why Stress Matters

Being on the hamster wheel is stressful and sadly we do not necessarily notice the symptoms as they build. There is no one way of recognising it and we all experience it differently. Stress responses start in the primitive brain which is unable to distinguish between a physical threat or an emotional threat and will therefore respond in the same way. A stress response, otherwise known as our *fight-or-flight* response, is essential to our very survival. How else would we know how to recognise danger if this response wasn't triggered by a part of our brain called the amygdala which is constantly scanning for threats? However, it is a primitive organ and as I have already suggested, cannot distinguish between real or imagined threats. Our bodies respond in the same way to a busy work schedule, a traffic jam or an argument, as if our lives were threatened and the hormone, cortisol, is released into the blood stream which makes us breathe faster, speeds up our heart rate and raises our blood pressure.

I think we would all agree that a healthy amount of stress makes us perform better and gives us that buzz but that buzz can become addictive. We may then want more and more until it becomes unhealthy and we start to display symptoms. Chronic stress can have an impact on every system in our body. It can affect our mood, our judgment and decision making, our immune system, our ability to sleep and our appetite, to name but a few.

Stress is one of the key health problems of our age. Much is written about it but what I want to do here is just give you a few ideas of how you can look after yourself. Because the key thing I want people to know is that there is only so much the body can take. You can read what happened to me in the next chapter. It happened for all kinds of reasons and one of the main ones was that I was not taking responsibility for myself. I felt, as many people do, that someone else should fix things and in some way I was a victim of a system: the NHS system. In that place there is no sense of choice and you feel stuck with no way to go. I wonder if you recognise any of this in yourself.

But we do have a choice. We have a choice every moment of our lives and at any time. You can choose for your life to be different.

Key Points of Chapter 6

- How I got onto the hamster wheel and some of the reasons why that may have been
- Reasons why women may get on the hamster wheel
- Why we need to get in touch with our feminine side again
- Why stress matters
- Some ideas and activities that will help you manage your stress

Moments to Ponder

Firstly, when you're stressed the physiological response causes your breathing to become faster and shallower. If you recognize you're feeling stressed just stop and take five deep breaths. Do that as often as you need to.

You may have started your feel-good list that I encouraged you to do in Chapter 3. Turn to it when you are feeling stressed and take some time out to do something from it.

Not long ago I came across the 5 ways of wellbeing. I think that they are brilliant in their simplicity. The National Economic Foundation, (www.neweconomics.org/projects/five-ways-well-being) reviewed some up-to-date evidence and concluded that these 5 ways to wellbeing were the most important in maintaining and improving wellbeing in everyday life.

The 5 Ways to Wellbeing

Give: This can be as simple as smiling at the checkout girl in the supermarket or saying thank you when someone opens a door for you, doing something for a friend or relative or even volunteering your time. Try and so something like this every day. Intentionally find the most miserable checkout girl and go and chat to her. See her face light up!

Connect: Really connect with your friends and family. This week call a friend that you haven't seen for ages, you know the one you keep meaning to phone and never quite get round to and go out for a drink. By connecting I don't mean on social networking sites or by text. I mean really connect.

Keep learning: Mahatma Ghandi said *"Learn as if you were going to live forever. Live as if you were going to die tomorrow"*. There's all sorts of learning. It may be a new skill, learning to dance or going on a course. What have you always wanted to learn and never given yourself the chance? Go on, do it now!

Take notice: Instead of worrying about the past or future, just spend some time being in the moment. I will tell you about developing a regular practice which will really help you be present in the moment in chapter 10 but in the meantime just notice what's going on around you, notice what's beautiful, notice the changing seasons and feel what's going on inside of you. Take time to do this every day if only for a few minutes.

Stay active: This goes without saying doesn't it? I think everyone is only too aware of the impact of exercise which causes the release of those feel-good hormones (endorphins). It doesn't have to be full-on but it does have to be enjoyable and within your fitness level. Take a walk or a short bike ride every day.

Make a commitment to yourself about how you are going to implement the 5 ways to wellbeing into your life. What are you going to say no to, to make it happen?

Stress is found in the negative emotions triggered by the feeling of not having enough time: anxiety, frustration and feeling overwhelmed. Recent research [10] concludes that tuning into our heart's intelligence can make a very real difference, as the heart has the ability to reduce our stress levels. So put your hand on your heart and feel the love for someone or something in your life that is easy to do. Feel it for 20 seconds and then notice how different you feel.

Activity log

What is my learning from reading this chapter and working through the exercise? ....

....

....

What actions am I going to take as a result? ....

....

....

By when am I going to have done it/them? ....

....

....

What is the benefit of accomplishing this action? ....

....

....

What is the cost of not accomplishing this action? ....

....

....

Chapter 7

The crash

So many of us spend so much of our lives on the hamster wheel thinking that we can cope, that we are strong enough to manage it, or that we're stuck on it feeling that we don't have a choice because of all the stuff we have to do. One of the reasons why I tell my story is because that's just what I felt. I didn't really give much thought to the damage I was doing to myself by the lifestyle I was leading, or whether I was actually enjoying it or not. I guess the adrenaline buzz gave me something! To have actually stepped off would have been a bit scary, as I would have to relinquish control of it all. Or maybe admit I couldn't do it.

This chapter is that part of my story where I fell off the hamster wheel and was given a diagnosis of stress related depression. It is also the story of how I coped at that time and ends when I made the choice to take charge of my life and leave a job I loved but which was damaging my health. I also discuss burnout. What actually is it? The chapter ends with reflections on choice. Many people, as I did, have felt or feel stuck, feeling that they have no choice in the way they lead their lives. The truth, that I hope you will see, is that we are making choices every minute of every day.

Heading for Burnout

I've called this chapter *Crash* but it wasn't that straightforward. It's strange, there is so much clarity for me about so much of what I have written but this period seems a mess of images. Everything started to feel out of control and messy. People kept saying you're doing too much. My family were unsure who would come in at the end of the day: a raging witch or the me they loved. It was more often the witch. At home I felt safe to rage and my husband was and always has been an absolute rock. I don't know what I would have done without him.

At work I just had feelings of being completely overwhelmed and unsupported. I kept telling them this job was impossible but they just would not listen. I felt completely uncared for and unsupported. Since our service had suffered seriously from disinvestment 2-3 years previously, a chasm had opened up between front line staff and managers. Somehow I was in the middle and I felt very isolated and alone. It would be unfair to say that I was unsupported, I had some very good friends who noticed what was going on for me but of course I wouldn't listen. People like me did not get stressed. It couldn't be happening. I remember accepting the professional lead post but, at the same time, expressing some anxiety. The previous postholder had left the post through mental ill health. I still question why they didn't learn from her experience? The urgency of that question has long gone. The NHS was not and is still not, in my view, a learning organisation [1]. In fact, from what I hear it has become a whole lot worse. How do people survive it I wonder?

The main thing I can remember at this time was not eating and, as a consequence, losing quite a lot of weight. Inside myself somewhere was a voice saying *If I don't eat then they will see my distress.* Well they didn't or if they did, no-one said. I felt out of control of everything, it was like books falling out of shelves. I remember using the back of my car as a metaphor for what was going on inside my head: it was full of work stuff and was a chaotic mess.

I was a hard nut to crack. I even got as far as doing my depression score using the EPDS (see chapter 3). I thought that maybe I was having symptoms of clinical depression but I chose to ignore them. In the end it took a friend of mine to wonder if I might have menopausal symptoms and suggest that I went for a blood test. This, at least, got me to make an appointment with my doctor. Thank goodness, I had an amazing GP who listened and listened to me for a long time. She suggested I saw a counsellor which I did and that was the beginning of my recovery. For 2 years (I thought it would be more like 2 months) I was in therapy and had the experience, probably for the first time in my life, of someone with an amazing skill of empathy. She really got into my world and it felt like she understood it. It was incredibly powerful.

One of the things that really worked for me at that time was her anger at the way I was being treated which helped me to see that it was not me that was in the wrong and that I was not a failure. She kept encouraging me to take some time off work and it did soon become clear that her help was not going to be enough. The final straw was a message I received on voicemail from a colleague berating me for not being there for her and my other colleagues and not playing my part in the team. I remember standing in the conservatory at home listening to this and I remember experiencing real distress. In the end my Director of Nursing insisted that I take sick leave.

It must have been July time I think. I went to my doctor's again and she gave me a certificate. Apart from one occasion I saw her regularly and she was fantastic. Sadly, there was one time she was on holiday and I saw another GP, who had no insight, couldn't see why I couldn't work and wanted to put *flu* on my certificate. One thing I always did was never shirk from my diagnosis of *stress related depression*. It was not necessarily sensible, I did suffer from the stigma attached to that diagnosis but I have always wanted to speak openly about mental health. I did then and I still do now.

Sick Leave

So I went off sick. The hardest thing was telling my family. Stigma again. However, I did and it must have been hard for them to handle but I had to be honest. I was off for 6 weeks, 2 of which were my holiday. What helped me was resting, music and walking. It was the summer and I would often sit outside and listen to music. Mahler became a favourite. His *8th symphony, Symphony of a 1000*, I listened to frequently. I have always found Mahler's music so powerful and it will always have a cathartic effect on me; full of despair but also full of hope. I also played it incessantly in my car. I did wonder why but now I think it was to help me connect with my emotions, something I was so unused to doing but in some unconscious way maybe I knew it was important. Like many other people I was not good at being with my emotions so developing an understanding of them was really difficult. I remember my therapist saying to me *Grieve, Ann, grieve*. I remember desperately thinking what does she mean? How do I do that? It felt as if it was a desperately important contribution to my recovery but I had never really grieved for the loss of my grandmother or my baby. I just didn't know how.

For the first time in my life I took myself off for long walks alone. I found out then how important it was for me to be outside in the open air. It really gave me time to think and it still does. Iain and I often go out for walks and those tend to be the times when we have the best conversations and the most insights. I also had a holiday during that time. We went to France, to one of my favourite places. The best way to describe the impact of that place is in the words I wrote only recently:

> "When all was madness around me, when I felt myself fast running out of control, this place gave me peace. Peace for 2 weeks every summer. It was the place I came to, knowing that here I would feel safe. It was a place that held me in its power for more than 10 years and it wasn't until I felt safe in the rest of my life that I was able to move on. But still I go back, back to the valley of the Dourbie with its waters running slowly, running fast providing a home for beavers and the eagles flying overhead, their vastness a metaphor for this landscape, both fertile and barren. Somehow it fed my spirit.
>
> The first morning we always walk to Nant that walk that I know so well and can still walk in my mind's eye, and see the brilliant blue flowers on the edge of the field, the globe thistles that scratch my legs, the fields of sunflowers and if we're really lucky, an orchid. We go round the bend and come by the river and hope to see a kingfisher but I never did. We may see a dipper skimming the water or other birds that love to look for the insects that inhabit the flowing waters. The path goes down by the river then rises high above it, sometimes in the shade, sometimes in the open and I feel the heat of the French sun on my body cleansing me, reinvigorating me.
>
> The shopping done, we take a seat in the bar where we have sat many times before and order beers and sit and watch this sleepy French village on a Sunday morning waiting for the church to empty out and our quiet bar to fill up with the locals, the same locals that we have seen year after year.
>
> We wander back along the same road over the bridge, back up that steep rubbly bit which is always hot because by now it's gone midday. The sun is beating down from that deep blue sky and in the shade at the top we drink some water and slowly meander back to our little chalet on the campsite that we have come to know and love and was my haven in the bad times. But now I look back with loving reminiscence at the photographs of the place that bore witness as I reached a defining moment in my life and gave me the sanctuary of its beauty, grandeur and peace."

But this particular holiday was not without its drama. We were there on August 15th, an important feast day in the Catholic Church, the Feast of the Assumption. I had long wanted to be there on that day as the village really celebrated in its own unique way and I wanted to witness it. It had another reason to mark the day as 2 inhabitants of the village were killed by Germans in a reprisal during the war on that same day. On the way there I tripped over a root and fell. Initially all I saw was blood pouring from my knees and then I looked down at my hand to see my thumb sticking out at an awkward angle. I had dislocated it. To make a long story short, we ended up in hospital and I had my thumb put back in place and in plaster. Such was the efficiency and the care given to me that we were back in our chalet in time for a lunchtime beer. Sadly, I have never yet been to the village of Nant to witness their celebrations. At the time I just felt more helpless and hopeless thinking that I had ruined our holiday.

As we left Cantobre, as tended to happen every holiday in those years, the tears came as I had to return to the reality of home and whatever awaited me. One thing I was learning through therapy was how my holiday acted as an oasis of peace in the madness of the rest of the year. That has now changed. I love my holidays but they have now taken on the characteristics of a treat rather than an oasis and I strive to take elements from my holiday back into my non-holiday life.

So we went back home and after a couple of weeks I was back at work. During the 6 weeks I had been off, I had had no contact at all from my manager. A bunch of flowers arrived from my Community Practitioners' and Health Visitors' Association (CPHVA) colleagues but nothing from my work colleagues, not even a card. The flowers were lovely and it was a lovely thought but they were left at the front door. Could my colleagues not face me? Were they relieved that I was out at the time? Was that more stigma? It was as though they just didn't know what to say.

Back to Work

After 6 weeks I felt ready to return to work and my doctor agreed. I just went straight back. I did expect some kind of phased return but that didn't happen. It was straight back into the same old world. I really felt that something might have changed but no. Any changes that were made I had to instigate. As I said in the previous chapter I thought maybe if I shifted my caseload work from rural Cambridge and into the city near where I was based for the professional lead work, that might help. I left the practice I loved and regretted it. I would have been better to give up the leadership role but I had fought to get that post better paid and I was reluctant to give that up. I would also have had to return to part-time work, for which there were also financial implications.

It was as if there was something wrong with me; it was my fault so all change had to come from within me. I have since heard someone speak about *toxic work environments* and the person who gets ill is like the canary in the mines who acts as an early warning for gas leaks by being killed by it. At that point I felt it was my fault and there was no one apart from my therapist to make me think otherwise.

So life went on for another 18 months and I began to notice my symptoms return. The most worrying one was not eating, particularly at work. I lost weight. It got to the point when I was with one manager at a meeting and she insisted I ate lunch. I think it made her feel better, rather than any concern for me! That night in the bath I tried to make myself sick. It was then that I knew I had to do something about it. I also found myself driving around a lot and playing Mahler in the car again, desperately wanting help but not feeling able to ask for it. It was some time during those 18 months that I completely lost my temper with my manager, something I have never done with anyone at work before or since and I have absolutely no idea what it was about. I had some very good friends and colleagues who were there for me at the time and that day someone did pick me up and dust me down. I will also say that my manager really didn't deserve it and sadly things were very difficult between us for a while and that was noticed by others. In the end we sat down in the pub one evening and sorted it out and remained good friends after that.

Sick Leave Again

It wasn't long after that in the spring of 2002 that I decided I had had enough and I went to my manager and said the most empowering words of my life: "*I'm going off sick and I'll come back when I'm ready*". I think we both knew that I would come back and hand my notice in. I spent the next month, it was a lovely spring, walking and reflecting. It didn't take long to come to the conclusion that I was not going to let anyone else do to me what 'they' had done. By this time 'they' were the NHS. Dare I give up everything? A good career, a good pension, a good salary and jump into the unknown territory of self-employment? But that's just what I did do. I think most people thought I was mad. Iain supported me all the way. He had done it and he saw no reason why I shouldn't. To be fair I did stay in part-time work in the NHS for another 4 years before finally severing the umbilical cord that joined me to it. I even had one final go at keeping the job I loved by making it into something manageable: I wrote a proposal for a nurse consultant job! That was laughed out of court!

So I went back to work and handed in my notice, I really thought that that would create some kind of reaction! But no! This time I ensured I had a phased return which was helpful. I was told to stop all my professional lead work but I refused. I couldn't just leave it. The absolutely awful thing in this period was my feeling of complete isolation. None of the senior managers I had worked closely with spoke to me to find out how I was or to say thank you. Most people had parties and leaving presents when they left but not me. I organized supper with friends but that was all. After a few weeks of this isolation I confronted a senior manager about my treatment and a card from the Director of Nursing materialised!

I now see that much of my experience at this time was due to ignorance and stigma, something I now speak out about.

I realise that I haven't mentioned Laura but the truth is when you're ill in that way you are the focus of your life. I bitterly regret that I neglected her at this time and I know she felt that. Some of her behaviour was awful, staying out late and not telling us where she was, I really felt that she was going to 'come off the rails'. Looking back from a more non-judgmental perspective, maybe we had done a good enough job and she didn't but it was during this time that 9/11 happened and she had to give up her job on an American airbase. She made the decision to go off to university to study outdoor education. In the middle of the course she went to America for 3 months, which gave her the opportunity to sort out what she wanted in her life. She decided to apply to do a photography degree. I shall always be glad we were able to help her do that.

What is Burnout?

What was this experience? I had a diagnosis of depression but was still able to function. I took the drugs because I was prepared to do anything to make me feel better. I see drug therapy as being a bit like a plaster cast; they give your emotions a break while you get the rest that you need. Was it a real clinical depression or a response to the events of my life that I had minimised and not dealt with? Or does it matter? What matters is that I was able to get the help I really needed through therapy and also by having a great GP. The drugs probably helped as they deadened my emotions. I well remember a year later when I started to come off them my emotions returning. I remember one incident in particular when we left Laura at Montpellier Station after a lovely week we spent with her in France. Tears of happiness at the lovely time we had had but also tears of sadness at her leaving

I strongly believe that the talking therapies are much more important than drugs. What saddens me is that it is accessible by so few, as so little is available on the NHS. I paid for my treatment and have no regrets because it was the start of what was a long recovery. I can't begin to tell you about the power of being listened to and really heard by someone who is completely with you and not judging you in any way. It enabled me to talk as I have never talked before and eventually to let go of the grief that I had been holding on to for so many years. I believe now that I was experiencing the early stages of burnout, particularly when I discovered this wonderful description:

"the desperate cry of the soul to break free, a spiritual crisis is a crisis of meaning, purpose and connection, and so is burnout." [2, p37-38].

The author, Stephen Wright, a nurse by background, is now running the Sacred Space Foundation in Cumbria, a retreat for people suffering burnout (www.sacredspace.org.uk). He sees burnout as an opportunity to take time out to see what the soul is crying out for. Others have also discovered that it can open a window for sufferers to discover a purpose which has heart and meaning for them [3]. Remember chapter 2 when we looked at your life purpose? This is why it is so important.

I was lucky enough to have that opportunity to evaluate my life and have now discovered real meaning and purpose in my career and life. I'm so glad that I was made to hear that inner voice because, without making the choices I have made (not necessarily easy ones), there was a danger that I could have remained a victim of my circumstances.

I have described my symptoms but for others it will be different. I met a lady with a long and dedicated career in midwifery but she woke up one morning feeling that she just couldn't do it anymore. It was some years ago I met her and at that time she has been unable to return to work. This is somebody who had immense passion for what she did but it would appear that she may be lost to the profession. Symptoms of approaching burnout include anxiety, insomnia, forgetfulness, inability to concentrate, feelings of being overwhelmed, frustration, sadness and physical symptoms such as headaches. Symptoms of actual burnout include calling in sick, not meeting deadlines, poor attitude, exhaustion, isolation and depression. All I can say to anyone reading this book is that if you see any of these symptoms in yourself then ask for help. You are not alone and you will get better. I have been told by someone who knows, the Sacred Space Foundation is a great resource for people suffering burnout.

Insights from the Experience

One of the most healing things I learnt was that it wasn't all my fault. Much of the initial insight came from my therapy and then from my master's degree which I embarked on with a degree of apprehension. With all that had happened I wondered if I must have been completely mad to start something which I felt would only contribute to my stress. I do remember thinking at the time that I needed to do this for me and I was intent on going forward with it. I have no regrets. The title of the course was *Nursing Research and Practice Development* which sounds really dry. It wasn't and what I loved was discovering theory to support what I intuitively believed. More important, was the discovery that what had happened to me was not all my fault.

One of the modules was entitled Nursing Leadership and I learnt so much. One of the things that intrigued me was the idea of a new world in which there would be an increasing emphasis on feminine values and beliefs such as caring, nurturing and intuition [4]. What a fantastic shift that would be for someone brought up in the patriarchal world of the NHS. It was also the first time I had discovered leadership theory and in the description of transformational leadership [4], I recognized the way I developed my role as professional lead. I didn't realise it at the time, it just felt intuitively right to me but it was clearly at odds with the transactional norms of the NHS. I began to understand why nurses were so downtrodden through reading about the behaviours of oppressed groups [5]. I read about the differences between healthy and unhealthy organisations [6] and about learning organisations [1]. I drank it all in. I began to gain an understanding of the complexities of what had happened to me and it really empowered me. My assignment included an Organisational Analysis, an opportunity to really reflect on what had happened and to learn. I also had to write an action plan and a vision for how my life would look in 5 years time. It was incredibly helpful and I gained my best mark of the whole course for that assignment!

Choice

What I want us to reflect on briefly is the issue of choice. It was the key thing for me which began the change from being a victim of my circumstances to taking charge of my life. So often we feel stuck in the way it is, we can't see anything being different until we move house, we retire, 'they' change the job description, the children leave home, et cetera. We are unable to see that we have choices but the fact is we make choices on a minute-by-minute basis throughout our daily life.

What we need to do is make those choices conscious and powerful as I did when I went to my manager in 2002. That way we can create a greater balance in our lives. Most of us yearn for balance, which is less about work/life balance because if you're in a job you love you then don't feel the same need; it's more about internal balance: balance within ourselves. Balance is also about living a life aligned with our values but with every choice there are consequences. For when I chose to leave a well paid job in the NHS, I also chose to walk away from a regular salary and a potentially good pension.

Key Points of Chapter 7

- My story through burnout
- The impact of therapy and drug treatment
- The beginnings of my recovery
- Making my first conscious and powerful choice
- Reflections on burnout
- How my studies gave me a greater understanding
- What really is choice and do we have any?

Moments to Ponder

Understanding our values is key to our decision making, so return to the exercise and notes in chapter 1 and reflect on whether your choices and decisions are in alignment with your values.

Do you feel stuck? ....
....
....
....

If you could choose to change one thing about your life right now what would it be? ....
....
....
....

What are the consequences to this choice? ....

....

....

....

What is the smallest step you could make to start this change? ....

....

....

....

Whether you choose to make that change or not it's up to you but what I hope you'll see is that you do have a choice.

Activity log

What is my learning from reading this chapter and working through the exercise? ....

....

....

....

What actions am I going to take as a result? ....

....

....

....

By when am I going to have done it/them? ....

....

....

....

What is the benefit of accomplishing this action? ....

....

....

....

What is the cost of not accomplishing this action? ....

....

....

....

Chapter 8

Acceptance and letting go

I know I'm not alone in finding the whole notion of change scary because change turns our whole world upside down, we have to learn new things, and try out new ideas and new ways of being. It has been scary and still is sometimes, it's been quite a roller coaster ride. Often it's easier, and feels much safer to stay with something that is really uncomfortable than step into the unknown. But I knew that I wanted something to change and that felt more important than staying in the place that I knew. It no longer felt safe and I did not want to be ill anymore.

I recently discovered this wonderful quote, which for me, defines the moment when I decided to embark on this scary journey:

> "And then the day came
> When the risk to remain tight as a bud
> Was more painful than the risk to bloom" (Anais Nin)

This chapter is about a journey within the journey that is the subject of this book; my journey of the last 10 years into the uncharted territory of an unknown future. It describes my personal journey, the process which I had to go through to enable me to move on with my life and maybe more importantly to let Laura move on with her's. It's about the process of self-discovery, personal learning and growth that I undertook. The following chapter recounts my professional journey, the journey that has resulted in the development of a business I love and ultimately this book.

What is Acceptance & Letting Go?

I have called this chapter acceptance and letting go because that is what I perceived were the tasks I needed to complete so that I could move on with my life. Even as I typed the chapter name I found myself asking what I meant by this. It's not something I could tell anyone else how to do and these are not processes that words can describe. One important *letting go* task was to let go of the *stories* I had made up and taken with me through my life that were holding me back. I had to write new stories so that I could have the fulfilling life I was yearning for. I had to learn to accept myself as the imperfect and vulnerable human being that I am. Over the last few years it has just happened, I have learnt to accept the help of those around me, in particular my therapist, my coach and others I have met on the way. They have helped me see who I am and I have learnt to honour and love and forgive myself. It has also been about learning about myself: what nourishes me and what nourishes my spirit.

The word *acceptance* is used in Elizabeth Kubler-Ross's grief model already described in Chapter 4. For me acceptance meant being at peace with myself. Acceptance about what had happened and accepting that nothing I could do could change it. There is much more to discover about both topics of *acceptance and letting go* in Carmella B'hahn's book *Mourning has Broken* (1). In this book Carmella, through interviewing people who had experienced hugely traumatic life events, identified 8 keys to help us handle adversity. The ones that I could really identify with are these:

Trust and surrender control: This is something I still find hard. I think one of the reasons why we find ourselves on the *hamster wheel* is because we find it hard to trust others and therefore have to keep control of everything ourselves but the consequences can be devastating. I had to learn first to trust my therapist who I talked to about things that I have never spoken to anyone about before. What a relief to let it go. Through coaching courses I have attended I can recall two experiences when I have had to trust someone in a rather different way. The first occasion was falling backwards and trusting that the person I was working with would catch me. The second occurred more recently in a tango session which was at the heart of a recent coaching class. I was led blindfold by my partner, in a crowded room, in a dance movement completely unknown to me. I had to let go of control and trust. So I've taken a few tentative steps in the right direction but the work is ongoing!

Share your pain and choose life: I stopped running away from the pain and accepted it (notice more acceptance here) and at the same time chose a life with greater meaning and purpose.

Find the hidden gifts: I'm amazed how often I have read about people who have discovered gifts in even the most difficult of life experiences and have put them to good and purposeful use. That is what I want to do with my story, because I know that other women will identify with what I have written, or at least some of what I have written.

Letting go was complex because there seemed to be so much to let go of. To do this I had to let go of the guilt that bound me to Laura and to let go of the grief that I had carried around like a lead weight for so many years. In an article I read, fairly recently, (2) I found this paradoxical and meaningful quote:

"Bereaved people may search and cling before finally letting go; but it has to be recognised that it may also be necessary to let go before there can be a genuine and lasting keeping hold".

The letting go felt to me like clinging to a rock face: I was frightened of letting go. I know that I have kept hold of something very important and that is the sadness that will always be a part of me; it's not there in an unhealthy way, but it is there. I know that it makes me a more rounded human being: someone who is able to empathise with others who have experienced loss in whatever way they have experienced it.

Learning about Body Wisdom

One of the most powerful things I learnt was to notice what my body was telling me. I noticed that the times when I was sick was in the spring. The times when I was at my most emotionally vulnerable were in the spring. It was the spring time when I lost my baby. It was as if my body was letting go in the only way it knew how and it is still going on. The first time I visited my GP with the stress symptoms, it was spring. The time I went off sick and made my big decision, was spring. In 2 out of 4 years that I have been singing with a local choir my experience of the spring concert has been blighted by virus infections.

I wrote the following poem one spring day, some years ago and I replicate it here because I think it explains it in a way that words don't:

My spring

My spring is a time of new life and new hope as blossom and leaves emerge on the shrubs and trees...
As daffodils and crocuses bloom...
As the songs of birds awaken me at dawn...
As the heat of the sun warms me...

But spring is also a time when a new life was snatched from deep within me...
A new life that seemed like a miracle...
A new life who I never knew, an amorphous 'it'...
Was it a boy or was it a girl?
Who would it have been ... 18 this year?
What sort of family would we have become?
Laura with a brother or sister ... not the only child, the stigma, the pressure she lives with...
Iain maybe with a son?
And me ... a chance to mother another baby, another child, another person...

The tears in my eyes as I write this, a symptom of the grief that is still a sadness deep within me,
The dark anger at the injustice, the unfairness...
After the years of humiliating investigations and treatment, the hopelessness and then acceptance...
A new baby ... and it died
What was the point of it all?

My body remembers even if my consciousness does not ... in spring
Five years ago the onset of depression and starting therapy,
Three years ago a letting go of grief, leaving my job,

And now?
Slowly ... slowly ... letting go of the grief, the anger deep within me

And I sit here listening to the birds,
Feeling the warmth of the sun, looking at the yellow of the daffodils...
And I can look forward with hope...
But there's a vulnerability, a fragility and a sadness that will forever remain a part of me

Ann Girling, March 28th 2005
Easter Monday, written sitting on the bench in the garden

It was also the spring when I experienced something really powerful that I am only now beginning to understand. I was at the christening of my sister's third baby, Millie. There was not room for us to sit with the rest of the family, Laura was not with us. There we were, just the two of us. No child. Everyone else had their families around them but not us. I felt set apart, different. Not only was it Millie's christening, it was Mothering Sunday: no place for me. I was not a proper mother; we were not proper parents. I have never felt quite so alone and so separate from my family. It felt to me in my aloneness that nobody seemed to notice; nobody seemed to care. There were tears and anger unable to be expressed. Iain felt it and he expressed it. We couldn't stay long, we had to go home. It was heartbreaking and I really felt I was going to break down. But I didn't.

At one time I was angry with the world, especially my family (something else I had to let go of) but not now. I now have to accept my part in this. I never asked for help, I never talked about how I felt. I never shared my pain. We can't expect people to just know; we have to take responsibility and we have to ask for help. What I believe happened was that this event acted as a catalyst that allowed me to start to let go of that grief. For which I shall always be grateful.

One thing I learnt from these experiences is what eastern healing practices are bringing us, that we must not treat the mind and body as separate entities but instead see them as an integrated whole. We are now witnessing a growing interest in traditional treatments: acupuncture, shiatsu, Chinese traditional medicine, to name but a few. I am fascinated to read about the growing knowledge of heart intelligence which suggests it is the heart that is the guiding influence over our emotions (3). I struggle with a lot of these ideas because of my nursing background but I want to be open to it because it makes so much sense!

My Personal Journey

During the next few years there was a lot of personal work: through therapy at first and then through coaching. There will be more about how I developed my career and my business in the next chapter but suffice it to say that the coaching training I undertook in 2004-2006 contributed hugely to my own personal development. Through coaching I became more accepting of myself. I had always felt that in some way I was different from other members of my family. Indeed I am but I no longer feel that that difference makes me wrong. In fact, I've learnt to celebrate it! I learned this through further training

I undertook in the use of the *True Colors* (4) tool which I now use with my clients.

As for Laura, she gradually moved on with her life and eventually following her heart and studying for a photography degree. She was so happy when she achieved it and now as I follow her career, I have no doubts about her talent and her ability to be a successful photographer. Soon after leaving university she met and later married Kevin, who works in the US Airforce. I know that those years throughout secondary school, through my illness and then university were hard for her but she has come through it and I am so very proud of her. I regret that I could not be there for her when she needed me. At times things were very hard for her but that was as it was; I can't change it. For me, all the years of bringing-her-up paid off when I saw her on her wedding day. She had the most glorious smile on her face all day. It was indeed magical and I was so proud and happy for her.

She now lives in Germany; she is very happily married to a man she loves and in a career that completely fulfils her. I can't see her that often and I know the time will come when she settles in the States; it will then be even harder. I miss her dreadfully but most of the time it's fine. We email, we talk on the phone and I can follow her exploits on Twitter and Facebook. However, I do believe that now she is able to be who she truly is; now we are free of the ties that bind we are able to truly enjoy each other's company. My pride in her grew this year (2011) when I visited her after the birth of my gorgeous grandson, Jacob. She is an amazing mother and what a time for me to finally accept that without the mothering I had given her she could not be the fantastic mother she is to Jacob. A very humbling experience.

Therapy or Coaching?

The processes that most helped me with this journey were therapy and coaching. I could not have done it alone. At this point I want to distinguish therapy from coaching as best I can so that others can make the choice about what they think will most help them. I believe that we can all benefit from coaching and I see it as a process of lifelong learning but *the majority of those who seek therapy are at a low point in their lives facing distress and emotional pain* (5 p26).

I remember reading somewhere once that everyone deserves coaching and I completely subscribe to the view that if everyone had a coach, the world would be a far better place. Patrick Williams (6) describes a continuum which I think is far more useful than a straightforward difference with traditional therapy. He is in no way undermining the value of therapy but his argument is that with the advent of the new option of coaching, therapy will increasingly serve only those clients who really need it. And that will make it more accessible to those with greatest need. First, certainly in this country, we need to get away from the automatic response to send someone to counselling. Coaching needs to be seen as a very real option for people who are feeling low, sad or stressed or whose lives lack meaning and purpose, to help them move to a place of wholeness and happiness.

This part of my journey began with therapy and built a great foundation for me to move forward. It was a hugely enlightening experience; first and foremost because it was the first time I had experienced the power of fully being listened to and the power of real empathy, someone really understanding my world. I was helped to understand why I responded to my situation as I did and I was helped to realise that I was not to blame for what was happening to me. To actually witness the anger of my therapist to my situation at work was incredibly healing. She was also able to help me begin to let go of the grief and it was unresolved grief which was the root cause of my depression. Therefore therapy was the right place for me to be.

Coaching, with its foundations in positive psychology has moved me forward to the fulfilling life I now have and to be as mentally healthy as I am. It has challenged me to step out of my comfort zone and to do the scary things that have helped me achieve more than I ever realised I could achieve.

Understanding Coaching

Another aspect of acceptance was the realisation that *I am enough* (7) and the self-confidence and esteem that has grown over the years has contributed to that. I know that both therapy and coaching have helped enormously.

Now I want to talk about coaching: something that is quite difficult to describe. I want to tell you a couple of stories about how I first experienced it. When I first went on the Coaches Training Institute (www.thecoaches.com) fundamentals weekend I had no idea what I was letting myself in for, I had spoken to a colleague who just said to me "*Ann, you must go and do this, it's what you do anyway*". (I will share more about how I arrived there in the next chapter.) So I went along and by the end of the weekend I was completely bowled over. The first exercise was an ice-breaker and we shared with our fellow participants our dreams. I had never really thought about my dreams. Dreams were things that you didn't really act on and seemed unachievable but suddenly I realised maybe I could do so. I remember talking about wanting to buy a house in France and subsequent to this, Iain and I did seriously think about it but made the choice not to take it further. We looked and I am sure that if, in that time, the house of our dreams had come up for sale, we would have considered it but it didn't and neither of us have any regrets because we gave ourselves the chance.

I remember on that same weekend, when one of the leaders coached me and said "*Ann, you are a powerful lady*". Wow, it was like a shot. Me? Powerful? Never! I was wearing a red cardigan which she commented on. I couldn't see myself as powerful: power didn't seem like a good thing to me. Through coaching I have come to learn that I do have power; the power to make a very real difference in people's lives. Indeed we all have power but it's how we use it that counts.

As I went through the core curriculum I learnt about my values, something I had never considered before. I learnt about making real choice. I learnt about how we can become stuck and how the saboteur can hold us back. I learnt about the endless possibilities there are out there if only we dared. I remember the powerful image of the green space opening up in front of me, in front of what resembled a Grand National fence and feeling very scared. I remember being taken out of my comfort zone by being challenged to sing in public and knowing, as I walked back to the station, tears streaming down my face, that this was a defining moment for me. The next morning I went back and sung *The Fields of Athenry* with my iPod as my backing group to an audience of 6 or 7. There wasn't a dry eye in there. This is how the experience continued; lots of learning which I take into my coaching but so much learning about me. More powerful than anything was the acknowledgement I received from my colleagues for which I am truly grateful. That work has continued with my coach who I have now been working with for several years.

I have now accepted who I am which enables me to wear the clothes I want, to accept and honour the body I have and be the woman I am. When I set up as a self-employed woman I had an image of how I should look. I had two trouser suits and a beautiful black briefcase that Iain gave me but somehow I never felt right. I kept my hair short to manage the curls. Now I have a pink diary but sadly the brief case is not pink but a rusty colour! I wear colourful clothes (a jacket is my level of smartness) and my hair has grown and its curls are flowing free. This has become possible for me, so I know it is possible for others.

Hence I decided to share my story and my journey in this book.

Key Points of Chapter 8

- What do we mean by acceptance and letting go
- The importance of noticing what our bodies are telling us
- Learning to accept vulnerability
- The difference between coaching and therapy
- Understanding coaching

Moments to Ponder

Letting go: A good exercise in letting go, is letting go of clutter. I found this definition:

"Clutter is the stuff in our homes and in our heads that gets in the way of us living the life we desire" [8, p158].

People with a lot of clutter are often tired and overwhelmed. First, ask yourself *What do I really and truly want in my life?* To have what you want you need to let go of the stuff you don't want! Start with your physical clutter and see what no longer serves you.

Right now or absolutely as soon as it's reasonable take 15 minutes (set a timer), put on some music and make a start. Choose a small area in your house. Here's some tips to help you

> **Not everything needs to be thrown away**: if you want to keep something it deserves a place where there's order. For example, I have a basket where I keep things that have meaning for me: an old school project book that belonged to my grown up daughter, special cards et cetera.

> **What can go?** Broken things, things that you haven't used in the past year or so: paper, odd socks, unwanted presents.

Then there's emotional clutter which may include:

> **To do lists** that rule us rather than help us
>
> **Old stories and self-judgments** that hold us back
>
> **Labels:** I bet you have all kinds of labels that describe you, some you want, some you don't want.

Write down on a piece of paper the things that you want to declutter from your head: take 15 minutes and just write. When you've done that I want you to write each thing down on separate pieces of paper and make a ceremony of tearing them up into tiny pieces and putting them in the bin. Have a friend round and do it together. This is where you start to leave the bits of your life that don't serve you behind

I want to declutter: ....
....
....
....
....
....
....
....
....

Acceptance exercise: I'm also going to ask you to start accepting who you are so I'm going to ask you to do an exercise which I was asked to do by my first coach and I have asked clients to do since. Contact at least 5 friends, family or work colleagues and ask them to list your strengths and ask them to write them down for you. That way you can look at them in times when things don't feel so good. And I want you to thank them, not make excuses or anything else, just say a heartfelt thank you and receive the feedback for what it is, the truth about you.

Friend 1 ....
Your strengths: ....
....
....

Friend 2 ....
Your strengths: ....
....
....

Friend 3 ....
Your strengths: ....
....
....

Friend 4 ....
Your strengths: ....
....
....

Friend 5 ....
Your strengths: ....
....
....

Activity log

What is my learning from reading this chapter and working through the exercise? ....
....
....
....

What actions am I going to take as a result? ....
....
....
....
....

By when am I going to have done it/them? ....
....
....
....
....

What is the benefit of accomplishing this action? ....
....
....
....
....

What is the cost of not accomplishing this action? ....
....
....
....

Chapter 9

Rebuilding

What does *rebuilding* mean? Many of us have been in a position for whatever reason when we feel we have to start again; something has happened in our lives and the house of cards that we have created comes crashing down. For me, it was like starting again. After all, the career I had carved out for myself and which I loved was no more. No more assumptions, no more taking for granted. I had assumed that my job would see me through to my retirement and that I would enjoy a reasonable NHS pension. All that vanished when I handed in my notice and it was not surprising, after all those years, that I was connected to the NHS by a strong umbilical cord that took the best part of 10 years to sever and for me to come to realise that I could lead a healthy life without it.

Many of us in the coaching profession use the phrase *living life on purpose* and view it as one of the key elements in a life of fulfilment. I guess that was what I was about to discover in this rebuilding phase. This chapter tells the story of how I rebuilt my life and in particular the story of my business and how it has arrived at where it is now. I guess one of the things I've learnt and what I want to share with you is that it is never too late to discover *the work you were born to do* [1]. It's taken me over 60 years but I have no regrets and it would serve no purpose if I did!

Setting out on Another Journey

So I left my job as a health visitor to set up on my own and I had this great idea that lots of health care organisations would use my skills to support them in practice development. No, that's not what happened!

I really had no idea what I was going to do. I had no business plan, just some headed notepaper, some business cards, a website and a passion to make a difference. I really had no idea about running a business! But I did still have a part time job in the local NHS and I did some bank health visiting. That gave me the security to get going, as it meant I always had an income but I can't begin to tell you how excited I was when someone I knew at the local university asked me to lecture health visitor students for the princely sum of £25. You'd have thought I was being offered the Earth and the time I spent in preparation bore no resemblance to what I was being paid! But it was a start! I have to say, that after that I was never out of work; whether it was work I was commissioned to do, paid work or bank work. I felt I'd cracked it! At the same time I was still studying for my masters and that included carrying out some original research.

My Research

I'd like to write a little about my research project because I think it had a huge impact on my knowledge and confidence and also because, in it, I began to realise what was really important to me in my working life. In common with some of the women I meet on a daily basis, many of you reading this book will have had the experience of a health visitor coming round to your house and I know, because people tell me, that some of these experiences are good and some are bad. Relationships have always interested me and the kind of *helping* relationship that forms the heart of good health visiting practice fascinated me. So that was what I researched in a project entitled: *What is the lived experience of health visitors working in long-term relationships with clients?* It helped me more than all my years of experience to appreciate what a difficult job health visiting is, because I was looking at health visitors' relationships with families where there were child protection concerns, domestic violence, drug and alcohol abuse to name but a few. A lot of people don't appreciate how hard this is and that includes the practitioners themselves and certainly it applies to many of their employers. Sadly, I have never written-up the research for publication. I did submit it locally but little notice was taken and, as far as I am aware, it has made no difference to the lives of the health visitors I interviewed and the clients they serve.

For me though, it was an amazing experience and it took over my life for the year of the project; typing up interviews and analysing data with flip chart and post-it notes all over Laura's bedroom. The constant writing and rewriting of what I was submitting. Fortunately, she was not at home at the time! I think that it was submitted in October and March of the following year I heard that not only had I obtained my MSc but it was with distinction! I found that researching a subject was fascinating and I am finding it so again. In writing this book, my research has been much less thorough but again the learning has been fantastic. Most of all I learnt more about working in a relationship based way and how doing that well can make such a difference in the personal and professional lives of individuals.

My Connection to the NHS

However, I didn't just walk away from the NHS. Along with setting up my first business, Develop Health, I applied for a part-time job in professional development and, as I have already said, I did some bank health visiting when the opportunity arose. I was still taking on too much and I was learning how difficult it is to say no when you're self-employed and you don't know where the next piece of work is coming from. But the difference now was that I recognised that I needed to and after a year I realised I couldn't sustain that level of work. I decided to resign from my part-time job. However, my boss asked me to stay on, on an even more part-time basis, working on one particular project. That project formed the basis of what I was then able to offer to other organisations and I began to gain credibility in that particular field. The project was to develop clinical supervision across 3 primary care trusts (PCTs) and implement some training. That was what I did and I have been able to use the workshop I developed much more widely. For anyone reading this who is not a healthcare professional, clinical supervision provides the space for nurses and others caring for patients and clients to gain support, reflect on their practice and to become safer practitioners. It was great, I enjoyed what I was doing and I loved being able to provide a much higher standard of work than I had previously been able to do and get paid well for it.

One thing I did struggle with, and it took me a long time to overcome, was allowing myself to have an empty diary. People in the NHS appeared to thrive on full dairies and it was a matter of pride to be busy, to not have time to take meal breaks, to live this full-on life. I look back now and just see the madness of it. I see, with sadness, people who never say no and the impact on quality that this façade of 'busyness' has. Because that is what it is, a façade, a way of giving oneself a feeling of worth. I know because I did it myself. Going to meetings gave me a sense of importance that I was unable to give myself. Being late was almost a badge of honour because it was a sign of how busy you were and therefore of your value to the organisation. There was even some bitchiness if you dared go out for a lunch break away from your desk, as if you were skiving in some way. It is suggested [2] that this kind of conflict exists particularly within the nursing profession who exhibit what is described as oppressed group behaviour. They feel unable to revolt against the dominant group, which, in the case of a nurse or health visitor could be a doctor or a manager and so they turn in on themselves.

There are two instances I can think of that I hope will illustrate some of what I mean by 'busyness'. I was attending a meeting, late morning, at the local PCT. By now I was working as an external facilitator and growing wiser and seeing things more objectively, when I bumped into an old boss who rushed in saying "*I've been to 4 back-to-back meetings*", again a badge of pride. But I was screaming out to say *But how are you going to act on any of them?* This was the same manager who asked many of us to support him in a project which took a great deal of commitment and time from many of us working in the front line, only to find it fizzling out when the next flavour of the month came along. This may sound like the words of someone who has been embittered by her experiences but I have to say that, although true once, it is no longer true. On a bigger scale, however, I am often angered by the sheer waste of resources that goes on in the NHS.

The second instance was when I was doing some bank health visiting. I arrived in the office to find somebody I knew sitting there waiting for an appointment with a colleague. For some reason I sensed rightly that she was waiting for her supervision, the only real emotional support staff receive. As I was leaving I bumped into the supervisor rushing up the stairs 20 minutes late for this appointment, a third of the time gone. What value did she place upon her supervisee and on the process? I was angry and all the time, slowly, slowly, beginning to distance myself from the unhealthy culture [3].

Becoming a Coach

At some point in all of this I realised that what I was doing was not going to be enough, I was missing that connection I had with my clients, so I decided to embark on counselling training. I recalled one of my old clients saying to me "*Ann, you ought to go and train as a counsellor*". There was obviously some appeal because I loved to work in that relationship based way and at that point I had never heard of coaching, so I enrolled on a foundation counselling course. The main thing I learnt in that year was that I did not want to be a counsellor! I didn't want to stay with people in their past, I wanted to help people develop and move on (as I had wanted for myself way back), to help them be the best they can be and to have the lives they want. I was becoming more aware of what was possible in that way of working through my supervision work. Then a colleague told me about coaching after she had been on the foundation course with the Coaches Training Institute (www.thecoaches.com). I immediately enrolled on the foundation weekend and bought the book [4]. I couldn't believe when I read it that this book described exactly what I was doing on a daily basis, whether it be with clients as a health visitor or with health care professionals in supervision, and also how I had worked with my colleagues as professional lead.

So in December 2004 I embarked on my coach training with the Coaches Training Institute and was hooked completely and utterly. Having completed the foundation weekend I wanted to go straight on and do the core curriculum. However, I had to be patient and wait for some time and money but only until the spring of the following year. Not only did the course teach me amazing coaching skills but, unlike the counselling course, it was all about personal development as well. I have to say that it was the decision to train as a coach that was key to rebuilding my life as well as my career. I was thrilled to be able to fund this programme myself and in August of the same year I went onto the 6-month certification programme. By the summer of 2007 I was a fully certified and accredited coach.

After completing the core curriculum, I set up my coaching business, Develop Self, with the intention of running it alongside Develop Health. I naively thought that if I put a few adverts around, clients would come clamouring to my door. Of course they didn't! Yes, I had clients, in the main from the NHS, many as a result of the workshops I was doing. Indeed, I have since come to realise that clients do tend to be people you have already had a chance to build up a relationship with. All I can say is that I was wowed by the results. Coaching is so much about the relationship which coach and client build together and then the coach fully listening to, seeing and acknowledging the client. I have seen clients take courageous steps to make changes in their lives so that they can confidently go for a promotion and achieve it or take their lives in a completely different direction or even do something that they never dreamt they could do.

Coaching is about helping clients fulfil their potential. Believe it or not, potential is something we all have and for most of us we haven't had the chance to discover it. But what is it and what does it mean?

Try this for a definition:

> *"Potential is a condition of having power that is potent and has not yet come into being; it is possible, latent, unrealized and underdeveloped. Our potential resides in our essence, the core or center of us"* [5, p25].

What a fantastic profession that allows us to develop that in all of our clients, to see them become all that they can be. Amazing!

Coaching can also help us get over the fears that get in our way. I have mentioned the saboteur throughout this book and one of the saboteur's roles is to keep us safe, to stop us taking that big step out of our comfort zone into running our own businesses, taking our lives in a different direction or going on trips that we never thought we could do; the list is endless but somehow I have done it. It's taken a lot of courage, trust and belief in myself and a lot of help, support and encouragement from family, friends, colleagues and, of course, my own coach. But there's always further to go, another hurdle to cross. It's not easy! It's definitely challenging and there are times when I have wanted to give up but more often than not, I can pick myself up and carry on because I am passionate about what I'm doing and I have goals and a vision so that I can see the way forward.

Still, the business didn't feel right. I was reading a lot about how important it was to find your niche in coaching. That made complete sense when I read it in the marketing literature. You can't please everyone, so by finding a niche you can gain credibility in your chosen area and then your marketing becomes a lot more effective [6]. But how was I to find it? I was very drawn to the NHS. After all I knew it well and I remember people encouraging me to go down that route. It made sense and I wanted to make a difference in the NHS but something never completely resonated with me. In 2006, the time came when I finally cut the remaining employment ties that connected me to the NHS. However, still the psychological attachment remained. It is only far more recently that I have found my passion, and therefore my niche, that I have been able to completely let it go. I know my underlying fear was that if I did let go, I may never find any work and it was the saboteur that prevented me from finding my focus and my passion.

I went into 2007 with a decision to declutter and focus. To be honest now I can't even remember what my new focus was! I remember deciding I was going to throw out a whole load of stuff and did just that on my birthday that year. My business went through yet another metamorphosis including a rebranding and a name change. Agenesis was born. The intention was to combine my coaching business with the work I was doing in the NHS.

However, 2007 was to prove a momentous year in my personal life as well. Iain and I made the decision to move up to Chester. We had always planned that some time we would, but we were always finding reasons why we couldn't. In the springtime of that year we finally made the decision to go for it. It was an extremely stressful process and maybe that is why I am struggling to remember the focus of my metamorphosed business, or maybe I just wasn't clear myself, which is nearer the truth I think! And it was the year that Laura got married.

Moving

So in December of that year, we moved feeling fairly secure that we would be able to pick up our businesses and carry on but what we didn't know was that we were on the verge of the deepest recession in living memory. For the first year I was driving up and down to London and Cambridge completing projects there, leaving Iain struggling with a house that had suffered from years of neglect and finding work very difficult to come by. 12 months later we were both in that position and there were times when we were really worried about how we were going to pay our monthly bills. We had ploughed all our money into the house. I was desperately trying to get entries into NHS organisations and I well remember the day when Iain said to me, "*If you don't stop trying to break down the NHS door, it's going to break you.*" That made me really sit up. The NHS had broken me once and there was no way it was going to do it again.

As in many difficult periods of our lives, there is always opportunity. I started networking and met loads of people who could see what valuable skills I had and they helped me realise that there was an opportunity in combining my health visiting and coaching skills together. Gradually my niche materialised and On the Threshold was born. Its aim was to work with women who had suffered illness, such as postnatal depression and breast cancer or had experienced significant life events such as divorce or redundancy or other conditions, such as miscarriage or childlessness. I wanted to work with women whose stories were similar to mine because I was so aware of the difference that coaching had made to me. I was aware that the experience I shared with other women was about loss: accepting that loss, finding the nugget in it, incorporating the sadness and then refocusing on the present and the future.

Developing a Vision

But what valuable lessons I had learnt! From my experience of running a business I realised that if this business was going to be big I needed help. Both Iain and I had been reading much more about businesses and business growth and were both impressed by the need to work on your business rather than just in it [7]. I knew my knowledge of marketing was patchy to say the least, so I found someone to help me with that. I also needed someone to develop a brand that was memorable and strong, so again I found someone. In July 2009 the new website went live. However, I still insisted on keeping my other business going. The fear remained that if I closed it down I would never make any money. I clearly didn't have the faith in my new business and the focus was still lacking.

Sometimes we just need to have the courage to do what we know to be intuitively right and I needed help with that too. Early in 2010 my lovely friend, Sallie, gave me the kick I needed simply by suggesting that I run group coaching for women. I had this weird experience of falling in love with my business and feeling a bit like I did when falling in love for the first time. From then the work started slowly to come in, I went to speak in the places that I felt intuitively were right for me and to meet the people that I knew could help me achieve my goals. I became very goal focused.

My vision is definitely growing and every so often I think I'm there and then something else happens. I was again beginning to see my business in a slightly different way and I was incredibly reassured when I heard someone speak recently who said, "*Ladies, you need to reinvent yourself every day*". Underpinning my desire to work with women is the strong belief that if women have the chance to develop themselves to their full potential, then they have the power to make a real difference in the world. I had struggled to assimilate that with my chosen niche. I was also finding that the women who were finding me were coming to me because they were at a crossroads or on the hamster wheel that I described in chapter 6 or were having a crisis of confidence. What I now realise is that women will come to coaching when they're ready for change and to discover what their potential is and that all of what I have described above is important. Life gets in the way of us developing that potential, whether it be having a family, an illness, stress or a life-changing event like divorce or redundancy which can mean we lose focus.

So there you have it: the evolving *On the Threshold*. And in the final chapter you will see how it has continued to evolve.

Key Points of Chapter 9

- My professional journey 2002-2010
- Letting go of the NHS
- Building businesses and finding a niche
- The importance of a vision and goals

Moments to Ponder

Setting Goals

Without goals you are not going to get to that vision. Some of it you can have right now if you choose. Set goals for the next 12 months making sure they are Coaches Training Institute [4] SMART goals (and not SMART as in the traditional way):

Specific: you know exactly what these goals mean.

Measurable: you can measure when you've done them.

Accountable: do you have anyone like a coach, partner, friend who you can share your goals with and who can hold you accountable?

Resonant: are these goals resonant with your values, your life purpose or are they full of oughts and shoulds? If it is the latter, tear them up and start again.

Thrilling: they need to make you excited, even be a bit scary.

And every morning ask yourself *What 3 things can I do today that will help me achieve these goals?*

Creating a Vision Board

Right now I want to help you develop your vision of how you want your life to be. Throughout this book I have asked you questions or given you homework to help you find out more about yourself and what you want. It's now time to make that come alive. One way you can do that is to create a vision board. The more you focus on what it is you want in your life the more you are likely to get it. Having a vision board will make what you want in your life come alive and then you can set yourself goals to get there.

Look several years, say 10 into the future, at a time of your choice, brainstorm all the things you want in your life. To help you, include some of these ideas adapted from *The Vision Board* by Schwartz [8]:

.... years from now (you choose how many) I live in (think about where in the world you are, the sort of house you live in, who is going to be in it with you) ....

....

....

....

I am surrounded by ....

....

....

....

My lifestyle includes ....

....

....

....

I immerse myself in ....

....

....

....

My world includes ....

....

....

....

I am feeling ....

....

....

....

I am grateful for ....

....

....

....

Consider your values and your life purpose and then get hold of some magazines, a large sheet of paper (the sort you had in your art lessons at school), scissors and glue and start creating a pictorial vision of your life 10 years hence.

Activity log

What is my learning from reading this chapter and working through the exercise? ....
....
....
....
....

What actions am I going to take as a result? ....
....
....
....
....

By when am I going to have done it/ them? ....
....
....
....
....

What is the benefit of accomplishing this action? ....
....
....
....
....

What is the cost of not accomplishing this action? ....
....
....
....
....
....
....
....

Chapter 10

Having the chocolate

This has been a story of sadness, loss and regret but also a growing hope, expectation and excitement for the present and the future. The final chapter contains a brief reflection on my journey, particularly over the last 10 years. It's also about the here and now and the future: my future and your future, by picking up and reading this book and taking time out to reflect on those *moments to ponder* you have made a choice that has started you out on your *journey to chocolate*.

Women and chocolate seem to go together don't they? In this book, chocolate is a metaphor for fulfilment and this book has been about my journey to fulfilment. It is intended to inspire and motivate you to do the same. I'm no more special than the next woman, so I know that with help, we can all discover what leading a life of fulfilment means for us and set out on our journeys to get there. The concept of fulfilment is something I will be writing about in this chapter: what it is and why it's important. I will also be sharing another concept that is increasingly coming into the mainstream of how people live their lives and maintain balance and that is mindfulness.

My Journey to Date

I have stopped and started this chapter several times already but the publication date is looming large and life feels so good that it seems like the time is right to finish this final chapter.

First, I want to spend a little time reflecting on my journey as I am proud of my achievements and want to celebrate my success. I can honestly say that what's happened over the last 10 years is a complete transformation. I find it hard to recognise the person I was 10 years ago. Yes, some of it has been very hard, particularly the therapy and then the coach training when I experienced a lot of personal pain. I have made some lovely friends and feel very blessed and I've learned loads. Firstly about myself, particularly through feedback from my colleagues and those who have coached me, which has enabled me to accept and value my strengths. I've learned a brilliant new skill, coaching, which I think is an amazing profession and one that can make a profound difference in people's lives. I'm also learning about business, particularly in the last 2 years, since On The Threshold was born. Would I have done anything differently? I sometimes wish that I'd done it all younger so that I had more time to build my business, but there's not much point in that because it doesn't change anything. My intention now is to enjoy the present moment and to look forward to an abundant future and hope that through this book and my work as a whole I can inspire other women to set out on their own journeys through personal pain to wholeness, happiness and fulfilment.

The Joy of Love

First, I want to tell you about where I am right now both personally and professionally. So far 2011 has proved to be an amazing year. You have read in this book my deep sadness at not being able to have more children and then the grief I experienced on suffering a miscarriage and the loss of my second baby. You will also have read the pride and joy I experienced the day Laura got married. Laura became pregnant soon after she was married and, she too, had a miscarriage. Then 3 long years went by as she also went through infertility investigations and treatment. I could hardly bear to think that my story was repeating itself in my daughter and I began to think and accept that I would never be a grandmother. So imagine how I felt when she phoned up to tell me that she was 12-weeks pregnant. I sat on the kitchen floor and cried! Jacob was born on April 16 2011 at 1.30 am and his mother's and grandmother's story make him a very special baby. I was awake all that night and keeping me company in the virtual waiting room was Laura's mother-in-law in California. I'm not sure whether Facebook ever expected to be used like that! Nor did I ever expect to follow the progress of my daughter's labour via the emails she was able to send thanks to an epidural! It was a long wait from about 9pm when she said that she was about to push, till the arrival of the news (by email of course!) that Jacob had arrived!

I went to Germany when he was 2 weeks old and instantly fell in love with him in a way that was very different from the way I bonded with Laura but was just as powerful. To use the phrase given to me by some friends who have also become grandparents this year *looking into the eyes of your child's child* is indeed a powerful and moving experience, especially when he smiles back at you! His coming into the world has, in some way, given me closure to the story that has haunted me for so many years: my sadness at being unable to complete my family. To see Laura having transformed into an amazing mother was both overwhelming and humbling. I know that the most crucial influence on our parenting is the way we have been parented ourselves, so to see her with Jacob has to be the greatest evidence that I wasn't the bad mother that I felt I was for so long! And to quote her blog (www.oohprettyshinyoverthere.blogspot.com) she calls him *her pride and joy, the best thing I have ever done*. I want the world to know how proud I am of her.

However, I had to leave them both and have to wait until August to see them again and that has been difficult. I often look at his photographs and have a quiet weep! But I can live with that just to have the joy of knowing that he is in this world and, for that, I am so grateful. I have become a Facebook addict. I go on there, eagerly searching to see if any more photos have been posted! You may remember me writing about the paradox of joy and loss in motherhood [1]. In a different way the same applies to grandmotherhood. I experienced the joy of falling in love as well as the loss of leaving him but the joy far outweighs the loss. His birth has truly changed my life and my priorities.

I have also been reflecting on my relationships with my parents and my siblings, particularly now that I am 'coming out' about my book with my family. For some reason I have kept quiet about it until now, maybe because it's only since its publication has become a reality and since receiving some wonderful feedback about it, that I feel confident I have produced something which is of value to others.

Since we moved to Chester, I have been able to spend much more time with my parents and that has been a joy. To have had this time with them is something for which I will always be grateful. It was a time nearly lost to me in the year after our move when my mother became critically ill. I was humbled to see her faith and determination contribute to her recovery. She is an incredibly strong woman and I am proud to be her daughter. She's also great fun to be with!

What I really want to say here and I have to be honest, there was a time when I was angry and wanted to blame my family for what happened to me but there is none now. There is only love for them all. The only person we can change is ourselves and we have to take responsibility to move from being victims of our circumstances to taking control of our own lives. Only then can we discover how much more fulfilling it is to love than feel resentful, angry or bitter.

Discovering my Purpose

Towards the end of 2010 I found myself becoming despondent about my business, wondering if it would ever be the success I wanted it to be. However, as ever, my determination kicked in. As I was driving back from taking Iain to the station one day, I said to myself that I would do whatever it takes to make my business successful in 2011. I had no idea what that meant when I said it but it has held me in good stead throughout this year so far. For me, success means making a very real and positive difference to the individuals I come into contact with and also to communities and the world but success also means that I am able to create a wealthy and abundant future for myself and my family.

Yes, I have worked very hard on various aspects of my business with the intention of building a platform from which it can really take off but the key thing that makes my working life so special is discovering my purpose. I remember my coach asking me sometime last year, *"Ann, what is your purpose?"* I think that's a great phrase; how do we know when we're living life *on purpose?* My experience having discovered it, is that you feel that life flows easily and you do have that sense of fulfilment.

To return to that particular day, I was struggling with this whole purpose thing. By coincidence, straight after my coaching session I was meeting my friend and colleague, Elaine Hanzak-Gott, for coffee. She told me the tragic story of Joanne (Joe) Bingley who had taken her life a few weeks previously as a result of severe postnatal depression. This had left her husband, Chris, grief-stricken and intensely angry at such a senseless waste of life. He committed to doing something about it and has set up a foundation in her memory. I remember the hairs on the back of my neck standing on end and knew that this was something I wanted to get involved with. I am now privileged to be a trustee for the Joanne (Joe) Bingley Memorial Foundation (www. joebingleymemorialfoundation.org.uk). We work towards educating and informing the public, fighting stigma and promoting best practice. To have these people be a part of my life and to be working together in service of such a great cause is a joy, as is the way we also laugh and cry together. I just know that this is where I can make my mark in the world. There are so many women out there whose lives are blighted with the legacy of guilt, sadness and low self-esteem and who, through the work I do, I can help.

I am also made more aware of this passion in my work with Elaine. We run workshops to help front-line professionals feel more confident about approaching women who may or may not have postnatal depression. We have an amazing synergy between us. On one particular occasion we were on fire: there was lots of emotion around and more than ever we were able to inspire the group to go out there and make a difference. It was one of those *peak moments* I talked about in the *moments to ponder* section in Chapter 1. It is when you experience one of those moments that you want more of them and that's when you know you're *on purpose*.

I am feeling that as I write this final chapter, in July of 2011, that everything is coming together in an amazingly synergetic and serendipitous way.

What is This Thing Called Fulfilment?

So what is this thing called fulfilment and why does it matter? Let's start with a definition which completely fits in with what I've been saying throughout this book: *a fulfilling life is a life of meaning, purpose and satisfaction* [2, p127]. It's also *about being fully alive* [2, p130] and it's different for all of us. There's a paradox here because fulfilment is not a destination, it's a journey. It's also something we can have right now if we choose a life that is in alignment with our values. Values act as a compass to keep us on the right track, helping us in our decision making and in our life choices. The *moments to ponder* section in chapter 1 will have helped you connect with your values.

Living a fulfilling life also brings with it health benefits. We know that optimism [3], positivity [4], happiness [5] and being in touch with your heart [6] all lead to a reduction in stress and therefore, better health. It all sounds very easy doesn't it, but if it was then we would all be doing it and people like me wouldn't have any work! All the processes of of life gets in the way. We don't stop and reflect upon what it's all about and we struggle to make difficult choices at times. Our saboteurs, with their constant chattering, can stop us making the changes we need to make or they get in the way of us stepping out of our comfort zones to have what we truly desire but that doesn't mean we don't or can't do it. I want to end this section with two quotes for you to ponder on which reflect the temporary nature of our lives and how easily wasted they are:

> *"Tell me, what is it you plan to do with your one wild and precious life?"* (Mary Oliver)

> *"Most of us get to our graves with our music still within us"* (Oliver Wendell Holmes)

My intention is to fully live my life from now on and play my music! Will you join me?

Maintaining Balance

Fulfilment is a lot about having balance in each area of our lives (work, leisure, relationships fun et cetera), so that the whole package seems fulfilling. By balance I mean something that is not static; it is something that we are constantly working at, as if we are permanently standing on one leg. What we want to do is make the act of balancing easy and smooth. It can mean something different for all of us and it may prove impossible to describe. There is that awful phrase 'work/ life balance' which I think is extraordinary, as it seems to suggest that work is something separate from life. As far as I'm concerned it isn't. I love my work and it is very much a part of my life. However, I have still found myself being bullied by my saboteur, who was suggesting to me that the only way to get success, as far as it was concerned, was by earning more money and the way to do that was to work hard and deny myself other things I loved to do such as walking, playing the piano and believe it or not, going to the gym. It had the effect of making me feel guilty about switching off the computer and choosing to do something else but I kept working at it and now I can make a conscious choice to switch it off and go to the gym or to the garden or for a walk.

To help us keep on the fulfilment track and maintain that balance, we need to build into our lives certain practices and structures. I know that I need to constantly work at maintaining that balance but there are days when things don't feel so good or I have one of those days when my saboteur takes over and runs the show. It's only too happy to come out to play and disturb things! Of course I get stressed, find myself juggling, wonder what on earth I'm doing and I can have a brilliant rant. I would hate anyone to think that life suddenly becomes a bed of roses. I want to be and am human, just like everyone else.

Mindfulness and the Difference it can Make

One of the key things that has made a difference in achieving and maintaining balance are daily practices. You may wonder what I mean by that so let me try and explain. I had been hugely resistant to indulging in something that really sounded rather strange because often the word *meditation* is applied to practices and I was quite decided that meditation was not something I was going to start. It would take far too long and I didn't have the time to do that! But the more I learnt about it, the more I realised that there was something in all of this and something that I could work with. Firstly, meditation is something quite simple; it's just about being present in the moment. We all do it when we're completely immersed in something and become unaware of what else is going on around us.

Let me tell you a little more about why this is important. Being present in the moment has long been seen as important by those who support Eastern spiritual and health practices but with globalisation and the opportunity for those brought up in the culture of Western science to experience something different, these practices are now being explored in the West. Together with advances in neuroscience, there is good evidence that these practices can make a significant contribution to health and wellbeing.

Being present in the moment is also known as mindfulness which, for me, is about stopping and being aware of the present moment and how I'm feeling both physically and emotionally. If it's not such a good day, it gives me the opportunity to ask myself, *What is it that I need today?* and to listen to the answer. It is something that we can all do but rarely give ourselves the time. Children are 'past masters': look at how quickly they recover from being hurt or how they absorb themselves completely in a task or learning a new skill. That is mindfulness and the joy of it is that it has a positive impact on our physical [7] and our mental [8] health. Here's a quote from Deepak Chopra, a well known authority in mind-body healing:

> "All of our troubles and all of our anxieties stem from our inability to sit quietly in a room for ten minutes each day."

I'd like to share with you what I do so that you can see how simple it really is. I will also confess to not doing it every day! In the morning I write my journal. Again, no big rules about what's right and what's wrong about journal writing. It may just be a description of the day or it may be more of a stream of consciousness, and I just write whatever seems to come out of my pen or it may be more about feelings. It just depends. Then I spend 5 minutes sitting quietly in my chair letting thoughts pass through my head rather than getting distracted by them, experiencing how I'm feeling and noticing what's going on outside. For example, I love watching the birds at the bird table. If I'm working from home I will go for a short walk towards lunchtime and then at the end of the day I may go to the gym or play the piano. In the summer, the garden is a wonderful place to be present in the moment. Simple, really. It's a case of discipline and ignoring the chatter of the *saboteur*! I have put ideas for how you might develop a daily practice in the pondering section of this chapter.

I wonder now if I was practising a form of mindfulness when I used to listen to Mahler in my car, when I was experiencing the burnout and depression. It was a way I could be with those feelings and I see now that it helped me become familiar with them and not fear them. In fact, in their familiarity, they almost became a comfort.

So What Next?

Well I'm not sure! It's about keeping on track and keeping my life on purpose. I am so excited about having my book published and stepping into the uncharted territory of being a published author and what that might mean. I have a sense that there are some exciting, fun and possibly scary times ahead, because I will be right outside of my comfort zone. But there will be the joy of seeing both little Jacob grow up and Laura becoming a successful photographer and also of Iain and myself moving into the next phase of our lives. I love the notion of abundance and I'm curious as to what it might mean for me and my family. It's a word that will hold something different for us all. I got some sense of it whilst on our 2010 holiday in the south of France. Here is an entry from my journal:

> *"Iain and I have been to look at and walk in the Cirque de Moureze, one of those creations of nature that is worth visiting. The setting is wonderful in the Herault Valley in the Languedoc in France. How glorious walking in the warmth of the sun, feeling the peace and tranquillity of the setting. Moureze appears to be a quiet, picturesque French village with a bar and a baker and a jewellery shop. Bliss. But I'd spent my jewellery allowance for the holiday! I was beginning to think abundantly, how wonderful to be able to spend more of our lives here. The thought of that house that we had once considered and rejected returned. Rejected in the past because we couldn't see a way to*

have it all. As we walked back to the car I spied a sign a vendre (for sale). I couldn't resist looking and both of us were smitten. There was a lovely French farmhouse set in a garden with palm trees and some kind of a pond and we loved it. You read about other people having these moments but never expect to have them yourself. I couldn't see how we could do it practically and financially and then I realised that we can get really caught up in the hows rather than holding the vision. It was Iain who said to me that we could live for 6-8 weeks there, have time at home and time visiting Laura and Kevin wherever they are. And then it dawned on me: abundance doesn't have a number attached, it's about possibilities."

We didn't go any further with that house, the financial *how* was not there but I have declared an intention that I will have a house out there in 2 years time (2012) and I can't go much more public than this! However, that means having a significant increase in my income. I want to be able to choose to visit Laura, Kevin and Jacob without having to count the pennies, nor do I choose to have an impoverished retirement. I want money and I want success and I want to achieve it through making a difference in the lives of women, particularly those who have experienced postnatal depression or stress-related illness, but also many others who have struggled in their own way. I want to help them recreate their lives and to rewrite their personal stories as I have done mine. This is what I want to attract into my life along with the love and fulfilment I already have, by using this mantra: *Focus, Action and Belief* [9] and I will maintain balance by keeping going with my daily practices. So bring on the next few years!

Key Points of Chapter 10

- Reflecting on my journey thus far
- The need to embrace love
- The meaning of fulfilment
- The importance of mindfulness
- Looking ahead to an abundant future

Moments to Ponder

The first thing I want you to do is to develop your daily practice. Here are some ideas. These are all about being in the moment:

> **Learning a new skill:** meditating, singing, playing an instrument.
> **Creating something:** painting, writing a book.
> **Lifestyle change:** exercise, going to the gym, walking.
> **Gratitudes and affirmations.**

Or you could incorporate this exercise [10] into your daily life to help a sense of calm be a more common and permanent part of your life:

> Find a time and a place where you can have some peace and quiet. Sit comfortably with your back straight and your hands on your knees or thighs.
>
> Now breathe deeply from your abdomen. Focus on your breathing and let any thoughts go by returning to focus on that breathing. It may help to count the breaths or to say to yourself, *I'm breathing in, I'm breathing out.*
>
> Continue for 10 minutes

This exercise is best done outdoors or at least looking outdoors [11]. The key thing when you're doing this exercise is to experience the world through your senses without labelling anything. In other words, without using your conscious mind:

> Look for about 15 seconds taking in the sights, colours and textures, then if you start to have a thought:
>
> Listen for the same amount of time absorbing the sounds then if you start to have a thought:
>
> Feel the temperature on your skin, the feel of your clothes, your heartbeat, your emotions. Taste the air, the breeze. Smell the air, flowers, the breeze.

Let me share something from www.thepowerofpractice.com about the importance of a daily practice:

> *"5 minutes a day opens a possibility, 15 minutes creates a change, 30 minutes builds a new path, 1 hour a day changes your world"*

So you see, even if you can only do 5 minutes that can make a difference. Commit to it for a month and then review it. You may choose to continue or you may modify what you are doing; extend the time for example or change your practice.

In the last chapter you thought about your goals. To reach those goals I want you, as part of what you do every day, to ask yourself *what 3 things am I going to do today to help me reach my goals?* But before you get too carried away and add something else to your probably already too long 'to do list', think also about what you are going to say *no* to in order that you can say *yes* to the things that really matter to you, the things that are going to take you towards your *chocolate* goal and use the F.A.B. principle: *Focus, Action, Believe* [9].

Activity log

What is my learning from reading this chapter and working through the exercise? ....
....
....
....

What actions am I going to take as a result? ....
....
....
....

By when am I going to have done it/ them? ....
....
....
....

What is the benefit of accomplishing this action? ....
....
....
....

What is the cost of not accomplishing this action? ....
....
....
....

Conclusion

Conclusion

So there you are, that's the story of my journey to a much more fulfilling life. As I think I have already said, fulfilment is not the end of a journey; it is something that we can have at any moment we choose as long as we make decisions and choices based on our values and not the shoulds and oughts of our saboteur's voice. It is something that we need to be constantly noticing by that feeling of resonance and flow when we are fulfilled and that feeling of dissonance when we are not.

When I was doing my coach training, at the end of each module we would have a session called completion when we said what we needed to say to make ourselves feel complete as if we have closed a circle in some way. It is also something I like to do with my coaching clients when we reach the end of our coaching relationship. So what do I want to say now?

Firstly, I want to say goodbye to the creation of this book now that it is about to become a reality. Now I can't wait to hold it, all bound up in its purple cover as I always imagined it would be! I never dreamt 2 years ago when I declared that I was going to write it that it would actually happen! But, you know, there's a lot we can do to make our dreams become a reality. One of the things I did do was tell a lot of people (including Facebook) about the project once I decided to do it and after that there really was no way back! There were a lot of people holding me accountable.

In writing the book I have discovered the first few ingredients of what will become my fulfilment recipe. I have shared some of the ingredients in this book such as values, choice and managing the saboteur. However, the ingredients list continues to grow and one of the ones that I am looking forward to studying in the future is resilience, the ability to bounce back when things go wrong and for us to discover our resilience stories.

Two of the ingredients that have felt of greatest importance for me, and which I've developed over the last year or so, are balance and self-care. Part of that has been developing the skill of mindfulness: learning to be present in the moment and the ability to be fully alive without worrying about the future or regretting the past. This can be achieved by adopting the daily practices that I encouraged you to do in Chapter 10 and keeping it going in spite of the 'busyness' and the doing of our lives, so that we don't lose sight of the need to constantly nurture ourselves.

One of the most important ingredients and one that may be taken for granted, is love. When I was reflecting on everything that had passed and the anger and resentment I had felt at one point in time, I was overwhelmed by the power of that emotion of love and realised if we can embrace it and feel it, all the negative feelings evaporate. I am reminded of music from Wagner's *Ring Cycle*: at the very end of the last opera, *The Twilight of the Gods*, as fire is raging everywhere, you hear the beautiful love theme rising up above all the other music. It's beautiful! It's worth doing the final exercise in Chapter 6 to really get a feel of what I'm talking about.

Writing this book has also reminded me of the need to look for the nuggets of gold in our stories of grief and loss. There will be something there for us if we look below the surface. I know that the work I now do and the story I tell is part of that treasure. When I look back at the miscarriage, it all seemed so pointless and it felt so hopeless at the time. It has been so important for me to embrace my own sadness and to appreciate that, having learnt to be with my own pain, I can be with the pain and vulnerability of others. I know that means I can make a real and powerful difference to other people.

Finally, I want to thank you for reading this book and hope that it has given you inspiration, permission and motivation and whatever you need to make the changes in your life so that you can have the life you want and also to believe you can be whatever and whoever it is you want to be and believe it's possible. That is why I wrote it.

Goodbye and make the most of your *one wild and precious life*.

Laura's story

When I read Laura's blog I was overwhelmed by it and I was also overwhelmed by the experiences she and I share. It seemed only right to include it here, with her permission. The arrival of Jacob has made an amazing difference to both our lives.

Wednesday, July 13, 2011

What a difference a year makes...

I want to tell this story, just because I hope sharing it will help at least one other person understand that happy endings do exist. I hope I don't sound condescending or patronizing because at no point is that intended, this is just me telling you the journey we took to get my beautiful baby boy. I also know there are many, many others out there whose journeys have been much harder and longer than mine.

A year ago (literally a year ago), I was vacationing in the south of france with some of my favourite people. I was relaxed and happy, partly because I was in the south of france, I mean who can't enjoy that but also because I'd given up on the idea of having a baby. I was no longer absolutely certain what day of the month it was, I didn't wonder in the days before my period was due if this was *the month*. It was an emotional roller coaster to say the least and being at the end of it was an amazing feeling.

Rewind 3 years and I married the man of my dreams (ok maybe not my dreams but the guy I love with all my heart) and one month later, as we were getting ready to pack I discovered I was pregnant.

And yes it was a shock, I mean we'd been married a whole month and we were moving to a new country and there was a baby on the way. Well, once I got used to the idea I was pretty excited. But honestly, looking back, I can tell you I never really felt very pregnant. Yes there were signs but nothing that stood out except that I hated the smell of corn nuts. Well we went to hear the baby's heartbeat for the first time and there wasn't one. Here I am in a new country, I knew no one and they were telling me my baby had died. I had a *missed miscarriage* and required surgery. It was a pretty tough time for me and my husband.

So we made it through Christmas and all I cared about was trying for another baby. It felt like it would make everything better. Honestly, I can tell you it doesn't and whatever we were doing wasn't working. And it sucked: it sucked because I knew I could get pregnant (and there wasn't anything abnormal in my pregnancy it just didn't work) but it wasn't happening. So then the stress sets in and as anyone who's ever had problems trying to get pregnant can tell you, we know stressing won't make it easier but it's hard not to. I mean, this is in theory what my body is design to do, right?

After a year, I saw a doctor and we were told we could be referred off base for infertility treatment. Then my husband deployed so everything was put on hold until his return that spring. I can honestly say, not thinking about it was wonderful for me. So he returns and we tried the whole deployment sperm thing – no luck – so off we go to the doctors. He has to do his thing into various cups and I have had more ultrasounds, blood tests and 'exams' than I care to remember. The result of all this was cysts on my ovaries and a blockage in one of my tubes for which I required surgery. So one laparoscopy, later they added endometriosis to the list and informed me *the best cure is to get pregnant*. Oh the irony of infertility!

So we tried 3 IUI's, none of which worked and honestly I hated it. I hated that I was having to inject a hormone on a certain day, that this wasn't how I dreamt of having kids and of how out of control I felt as far as my body was concerned. And then when all 3 failed and they informed us IVF was our only option – well emotionally I wasn't doing so good. Not that I would really talk about it but you can imagine these are not the words any woman wants to hear. Oh, and I was the healthiest I had been for at least 12 years; I don't smoke and I rarely drink (although I do love me a margarita).

I should say for the record now, if you know anyone having trouble conceiving, please, please don't tell them how easy it was for you and to 'stop trying' because trust me that's incredibly hard to do and that it will *just happen*. We don't want to hear this, we don't need to hear this and if you're our friends you will just be there when we need you.

So we stopped. I wanted my body back. I needed to just be me for a while. To love life again and enjoy my husband and I focused on my photography and spending time with the people I loved, including a girls vacation! I should just mention we had some wonderful discussions on our vacation concerning positions and Cassie was kind enough to demonstrate a couple (yes I went there!) and laughed and it felt wonderful to be me again!

So I return from France and my husband is in the midst of a major base exercise, working nights, so we barely see each other but it turns out we saw enough of each other. The planets had aligned or something and that week – no joke – I knew. I knew my body inside out, back to front and upside down by this point and something was different. There were signs; signs that scared the s**t out of me. I mean, what if I was wrong? what if I was getting excited about nothing. So I refused to do a pregnancy test, though obviously that wasn't going to help.

And there was crying, not my husband who was at work, he just said, *"well that's good then"*, but me crying, telling my best friend here who was the only person I'd told about the test. Well actually telling her husband to tell her *yes* cause she was in the shower and then crying when the doctors called with my pregnancy test result to say that yes I was pregnant and crying when I heard my son's heartbeat and saw his ultrasound (which by the way was the only day to my memory I have ever had high blood pressure).

I can't lie, physically my pregnancy was easy, the worst part was the round ligament pain around 4 months. But emotionally it sucked. I was worried constantly that something would go wrong. I quit running because I was scared and tired and didn't want to risk it and yes I packed on the pounds and I turned 30. My baby grew inside me, big and healthy and the *lil dude* had 10 fingers and 10 toes and I could feel him move and he got the hiccups all the time and I loved him. From the moment I knew I was pregnant I loved him.

And he was late. Now I know you don't want to hear about the birth but if you have to be induced, let me tell you pertocin is the devil. It is an evil, evil substance. Don't try and be brave and not take the drugs, get that epidural because it is amazing. Oh, and to all those crazy people out there who don't remember the pain, trust me I will never forget the pain. But it was worth it looking at my gorgeous, precious baby boy!

He is now 12 weeks old, and whilst I honestly hope no one has to go through this experience, the end result is something I wouldn't change for anything. The pain and the sleepless nights and everything else in-between are nothing compared to that feeling I felt when my son was born and yes I cried and loved him more than I thought possible. He is the most perfect thing I have ever done and as my friend pointed out, he is is totally *worth the wait.*

www.oohprettyshinyoverthere.blogspot.com

References

Chapter one

[1]   Serafinn L (2009) *The Garden of the Soul* Bright Pen, an imprint of Authors On Line Ltd; Sandy, Beds

[2]   Whitworth L, Kimsey-House K, Kimsey-House H, Sandahl P (2007) *Coactive Coaching* Mountain View, California: Davies-Black Publishing

[3] Rock D, Page (2009) *Coaching with the Brain in Mind* Hoboken, New Jersey; John Wiley & Sons Inc

[4] Oliver JM, Mooradian TA (2003) Personality traits and personal values: a conceptual and empirical integration *Personality and Individual Differences* 35(1) 109-125

[5] Miscisin (2005) *Showing our True Colors* Saint Ana, California; True Colors, Inc. Publishing

[6] Heelas P, Woodhead L (2005) *The Spiritual Revolution* Oxford; Blackwell Publishing

[7] Ford D (1998) *The Dark Side of the Light Chasers* London; Hodder & Stoughton

Chapter two

[1]   Menzies I (1960) A case study of the functioning of social systems as a defence against anxiety in Rafferty AM, Traynor M (2002) *Exemplary Research for Nursing & Midwifery* London; Routledge

[2]   Rafferty AM, Traynor M (2002) *Exemplary Research for Nursing & Midwifery* London; Routledge

[3]   Hawkins P, Shohet R (2006) *Supervision in the Helping Professions* Maidenhead: Open University Press

[4]   Girling A (2009) On Vulnerability *Community Practitioner* 82(11) 18

[5]   Snow C, Willard D (1989) *I'm Dying to Take Care of you* Redmond, USA; Professional Counselor Books

[6]   Silsbee D (2007) *The Mindful Coach* Marshall, NC; Ivy River Press

[7]   Whitworth L, Kimsey-House K, Kimsey-House H, Sandahl P (2007) *Coactive Coaching* Mountain View, California: Davies-Black Publishing

[8]   Williams N www.inspired-entrepreneur.com

[9] Cook M-L *Stop Resisting Your Success* www.inspired-entrepreneur.com/Articles/Stop-Resisting-Your-Success.aspx (Downloaded 09/06/2010)

[10] Brown B (2010) *The Gifts of Imperfection* Minnesota: Hazelden

Chapter three

[1] Whitworth L, Kimsey-House K, Kimsey-House H, Sandahl P (2007) *Coactive Coaching* Mountain View, California: Davies-Black Publishing

[2] Carson (2003) *Taming Your Gremlin* New York; Harper Collins

[3] Jeffers S (2007) *Feel the Fear and Do it Anyway* Vermilion

[4] Cameron J (1995)*The Artists Way* London: Pan Books

[5] Carter FA, Frampton CMA, Mulder RT (2006) Cesarean section and postpartum depression: a review of the evidence examining the link *Psychosomatic Medicine* 68 321-330

[6] Fisher J, Astbury J & Smith A (1997) Adverse psychological impact of operative obstetric interventions: a prospective longitudinal study *Australian and New Zealand Journal of Psychiatry* 31(5) 728-738

[7] Fisher JRW, Stanley RO, Burrows GD (1990) Psychological adjustment to Caeserian delivery: a review of the evidence *Journal of Psychosomatic Obstetrics & Gynaecology* 11(2) 91-106

[8] Shields B (2005) *Down Came the Rain* London; Penguin Books Ltd

[9] Swain JE, Tasgin E, Mayes LC, Feldman R, Constable RT, Leckman JF (2008) Maternal brain response to own baby-cry is affected by cesar section delivery *Journal of Child Psychology & Psychiatry* 49 (10) 1042-52

[10] Brazelton TB, Nugent JK (1995) *Neonatal Behavioural Assessment Scale 3rd edition* London: Mac Keith Press

[11] Murray L, Andrews L (2009) *The Social Baby* Richmond; The Children's Project

[12] Underdown A, Barlow J, Chung V, Stewart-Brown S (2009) Massage intervention for promoting mental & physical health in infants under six months (Review) *Cochrane Library* Issue 1

[13] Nicolson P (2001) *Postnatal Depression facing the paradox of loss, happiness and motherhood* Chichester: John Wiley & Sons

[14] Murray L, Cooper PJ (1997) Effects of postnatal depression on infant development *Archives of Diseases in Childhood* 77 99-101

[15] Dalfen A (2009) *When Baby Brings the Blues* Ontario, Canada; John Wiley & Sons Canada Ltd

[16] Hanzak E (2005) *Eyes Without Sparkle* Oxford: Radcliffe Publishing

Chapter four

[1] Simons HF (1995) *Wanting Another Child* 2007 Edition San Francisco: Jossey-Bass Publishers

[2] Bowman T (1997) Facing loss of dreams: a special kind of grief *International Journal of Palliative Nursing* 3(2) 76-80

[3] Puddifoot JE, Johnson MP (1997) The legitimacy of grieving: the partner's experience at miscarriage *Social Science & Medicine* 45(6) 837-845

[4] Rock D, Page (2009) *Coaching with the Brain in Mind* Hoboken, New Jersey; John Wiley & Sons Inc

[5] Gilbert E (2006) *Eat, Pray, Love* New York; Penguin Books

[6] Brown B (2010) *The Gifts of Imperfection* Center City, Minnesota; Hazelden

[7] Simmons A (2008) *Quantum Skills for Coaches* Evesham UK; Word 4 Word

[8] Whitworth L, Kimsey-House K, Kimsey-House H, Sandahl P (2007) *Coactive Coaching* Mountain View, California: Davies-Black Publishing

Chapter five

[1] Nicolson P (2001) *Postnatal Depression facing the paradox of loss, happiness and motherhood* Chichester: John Wiley & Sons

[2] Simons HF (1995) *Wanting Another Child* 2007 Edition San Francisco: Jossey-Bass Publishers

[3] Gerhardt S (2004) *Why Love Matters: how Affection shapes a Baby's Brain* Hove, East Sussex; Brunner-Routledge

[4] Ratnapalan S (2009) To be good enough *Can Fam Physician* 55(3) 239-240

[5] Brown B (2010) *The Gifts of Imperfection* Center City, Minnesota: Hazelden

[6] Gregg (1993) "Choice" as a double-edged sword: information, guilt and mother-blaming in a high-tech age *Womens Health* 20(3) 53-73

[7] Pease A, Pease B (2001) *Why Men Don't Listen & Women Can't Read Maps* London: Orion Books Ltd

[8] Heath, S (2008) *The essence of Womanhood* Cornwall: Ecademy Press

[9] Frederickson B (2009) *Positivity* Oxford: Oneworld Publications

[10] Seligman M (2002) *Authentic Happiness* Great Britain; Nicholas Brealey Publishing

[11] Hay, L I. (1997) *Empowering Women* London; Hodder & Stoughton

Chapter six

[1] Simons HF (1995) *Wanting Another Child* 2007 Edition San Francisco: Jossey-Bass Publishers

[2] Murray L, Cooper PJ (1997) Effects of postnatal depression on infant development *Archives of Diseases in Childhood* 77 99-101

[3] Center on the Developing Child at Harvard University (2009) *Maternal Depression can Undermine the Development of Young children: working paper No.8.* www.developingchild.harvard.edu

[4] Avan B, Richter LM, Ramchandani PG, Norris SA, Stein A (2010) Maternal postnatal depression and children's growth and behaviour during

the early years of life: exploring the interaction between physical and mental health *Archives of Disease in Childhood* doi:10.1136/adc.2009.164848

[5] Morrell CJ, Warner R, Slade P, Dixon S, Walters S, Paley G, Brugha T (2009) Psychological interventions for postnatal depression: cluster randomised trial and economic evaluation. The PONDER trial *Health Technology assessment* 13(30) 1-176

[6] Brugha TS, Morrell CJ, Slade P, Walters SJ (2011) Universal prevention of depression in women postnatally: cluster randomized trial evidence in primary care *Psychological Medicine* 41 739-748

[7] Lloyd J (2010)*Stress: A Literature Review* (University of Manchester: Unpublished)

[8] Heath, S (2008) *The Essence of Womanhood* Cornwall: Ecademy Press

[9] Watson J (1999) *Postmodern Nursing and Beyond* London; Churchill Livingstone

[10]Childre D, Martin H (2000) *The Heartmath Solution* New York; Harper Collins

Chapter seven

[1] Senge P (1990) *The Fifth Discipline: the Art and Practice of the Learning Organization* Century Business, London

[2] Wright S (2005) *Reflections on Spirituality and Health* London: Whurr Publishers

[3] Casserley T & Megginson D (2008) Feel the burn ... *Coaching at Work* 3(4) 24-27

[4] Barker AM, Young CE (1994) Transformational Leadership: the Feminist Connection in Postmodern Organizations in Hein EC (1998) *Contemporary Leadership Behavior: Selected Readings (5th Edition)* Lippincott pp 70-78

[5] Roberts SJ (1993) Oppressed group behaviour: implications for nursing *Advances in Nursing Science* 5(4) 21-30

[6] Bruhn JG, Chesney AP (1998) Diagnosing the Health of Organizations in Hein EC (1998) *Contemporary Leadership Behaviour: Selected Readings (5th Edition)* Lippincott pp 284-294

Chapter eight

[1] B'hahn C (2002) *Mourning has Broken Bath*: Crucible Publishers

[2] Walter T (1997) Letting go and keeping hold: a reply to Stroebe *Mortality* 2(3) 263-265

[3] Childre D, Martin H (2000) *The Heartmath Solution* New York; Harper Collins

[4] www.truecolorsuk.com

[5] Grodzki L, Allen W (2005) *The Business and Practice of Coaching* New York: WW Norton & Co Ltd

[6] Williams P (2007) Border *Line Choice* 5(3) 22-26

[7] Brown B (2010) *The Gifts of Imperfection* Center City, Minnesota: Hazelden

[8] Carlyle M-C (2009) *How to Become a Money Magnet* Marie-Claire Carlyle Broad-Davies

Chapter nine

[1] Williams N (2000) *The Work we were Born to do* Elements Books Ltd, Shaftesbury, Dorset.

[2] Roberts SJ (1993) Oppressed group behavior: implications for nursing *Advances in Nursing Science* 5(4) 21-30

[3] Bruhn JG, Chesney AP (1998) Diagnosing the Health of Organizations in Hein EC (1998) *Contemporary Leadership Behavior: Selected Readings (5th Edition)* Lippincott pp 284-294

[4] Whitworth L, Kimsey-House K, Kimsey-House H, Sandahl P (2007) *Coactive Coaching* Mountain View, California: Davies-Black Publishing

[5] Harvey J (2010) Aligning Performance and Potential *Choice* 8(3)

[6] McNamara H (2007) *Niche Marketing for Coaches* London: Thorogood

[7] Gerber ME (1995) *The E Myth Revisited* New York; Harper Collins

[8] Schwartz J (2008) *The Vision Board* New York; Collins Design

Chapter ten

[1] Nicolson P (2001) *Postnatal Depression facing the paradox of loss, happiness and motherhood* Chichester: John Wiley & Sons

[2] Whitworth L, Kimsey-House K, Kimsey-House H, Sandahl P (2007) *Coactive Coaching* Mountain View, California: Davies-Black Publishing

[3] Rock D, Page (2009) *Coaching with the Brain in Mind* Hoboken, New Jersey; John Wiley & Sons Inc

[4] Frederickson B (2009) *Positivity* Oxford: Oneworld Publications

[5] Seligman M (2002) *Authentic Happiness* London: Nicholas Brealey Publishing

[6] Childre D, Martin H (2000) *The Heartmath Solution* New York; Harper Collins

[7] Williams P (2007) Coaching from the Inside Out *Choice* 5(2) 41-42

[8] Williams M, Teasdale J, Segal Z, Kabat-Zinn J (2007) *The Mindful Way through Depression* New york, London: The Guilford Press

[9] Carlyle M-C (2009) *How to Become a Money Magnet* Marie-Claire Carlyle Broad-Davies

[10] Simmons A (2008) *Quantum Skills for Coaches* Evesham UK; Word 4 Word

[11] Heath, S (2008) *The Essence of Womanhood* Cornwall: Ecademy Press

Biography

Ann Girling worked as a health visitor in the NHS for many years until, suffering from stress-related depression, she chose to leave and work for herself. Since then she has been on her own journey to fulfilment both in her personal and professional life. She trained to become a qualified and accredited coach, setting up her business, On The Threshold, in 2009 at the age of 59. She also followed a long held dream and relocated to Chester and now, particularly since becoming a grandmother, is just relishing her life. The reason for telling her story and including the *moments to ponder* at the end of each chapter, is to inspire other women to make the changes in their lives so that they too can have the lives they want.

Apart from her coaching business, Ann is a speaker at a range of events and in her talks, she uses her story to illustrate the importance of mental and emotional wellbeing but also to give the message that it is never too late to make changes to your life or your career.

Through her years of experience, both personal and professional, Ann has become accepted as an expert in the field of postnatal depression in which she has co-authored a chapter for a book and is a co-facilitator providing workshops for front-line professionals. She also has a growing knowledge and expertise in the field of emotional and mental wellbeing. Her coaching speciality is helping women move on from postnatal illness and stress related depression to a life of wholeness and happiness again. She is a trustee for the Joe (Joanne) Bingley Memorial Foundation (www.joebingleymemorialfoundation. org.uk) and a postnatal depression expert for the internet advice set: www.greatvine.com

Contact details:
Website: www.onthethreshold.co.uk
Email: ann@onthethreshold.co.uk
Phone: 01244 300391 – 07787 56869
Twitter: www.twitter.com/AnnGirling
Facebook: www.facebook.com/OnTheThreshold
Linked In: www.linkedin.com/in/anngirling